THE HOME WORKSHOP SERIES

THE CIRCULAR SAW

RAY E. HAINES • JOHN V. ADAMS • JOHN G. MILLER
ROBERT L. THOMPSON • RAYMOND VAN TASSEL
Department of Vocational Education, New York University

D. VAN NOSTRAND COMPANY, INC.
NEW YORK • TORONTO • LONDON

NEW YORK

D. Van Nostrand Company, Inc., 250 Fourth Avenue, New York 3

TORONTO

D. Van Nostrand Company (Canada), Ltd., 25 Hollinger Road, Toronto

LONDON

Macmillan & Company, Ltd., St. Martin's Street, London, W.C. 2

10532a25

PRINTED IN THE UNITED STATES OF AMERICA

Preface

This book has a threefold purpose: (1) to describe the circular saw; (2) to explain both the basic and advanced operations performed with the circular saw; (3) to give, in detail, plans and explanations for projects the making of which is especially suitable to the circular saw. It has been written for the home craftsman and the beginner who wish to acquire safe and skillful technique when operating the circular saw.

The organization of the book is designed so that the reader is first familiarized with the saw itself: its construction and principle of operation, as well as its care and maintenance. Then the operations performed with the saw are explained, the basic ones first, followed by the more advanced. Illustrations that emphasize proper technique are used frequently to supplement the written explanation. Finally, the projects are presented, proceeding from the simple to the more elaborate. The construction of each project is detailed both by plan drawings and written explanations. Pictures are used to help the reader visualize the finished article.

Mention should be made of the book's format. A large page with a large type was chosen so that the explanations and illustrations would be easily legible to the reader under shop conditions. In the project section, the explanation of the projects, when the book lies open, appears side by side with the appropriate plan drawings. In this way, the authors hope the reader will find great convenience when he is working on a particular project explained in the book.

Acknowledgment is given for the services of Mr. Elliott Polansky in preparing the drawings. Mr. Polansky stepped in most opportunely to replace Mr. Carlton Bauer, who was called back to service in the Armed Forces.

R. E. H.

Contents

CONTENTS

I

History of the Circular Saw and Its Basic Principles

The saw is a multi-toothed blade used to cut a material by moving the cutting teeth rapidly against the material. If the cutting blade is a steel disk, the saw is known as a circular saw. The basic elements of a circular saw machine are:

a. A multi-toothed steel disk fastened to an arbor which is free to revolve in suitable bearings (*A* of Fig. 1-1).
b. A source of power as a means of rotating this arbor (*B* of Fig. 1-1).
c. A suitable unit or table for supporting and guiding the work piece as it is moved past the rotating saw (*C* of Fig. 1-1).

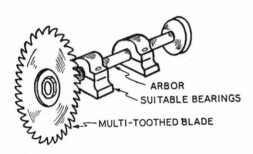

ARBOR
SUITABLE BEARINGS
MULTI-TOOTHED BLADE

(a) SAW, ARBOR AND BEARINGS

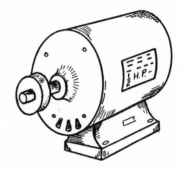

(b) ELECTRIC MOTOR (POWER)

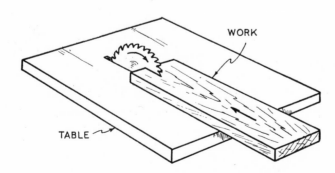

WORK

TABLE

(c) TABLE FOR SUPPORTING THE WORK

FIG. 1-1 Fundamental principles of the circular saw.

1

FIG. 1-2   Animal power used in medieval times to operate reciprocating saw machines.

Basic Principles of the Circular Saw. The term *circular saw* as it is used by the craftsman has a dual meaning. It may refer only to the circular cutting blade or it may identify the entire assembled machine. Historically, the hand saw is one of the earliest tools known to man. The first appearance of a hand saw with notched teeth has been traced in early Egyptian history. The oldest known specimen of an iron saw was used by the Assyrians in the seventh century and for hundreds of years there was little change in the design of this basic tool of the craftsman.

The first major improvement in the method of cutting materials with saws came with the application of power to a crude machine. Water, wind, steam, or animals were harnessed for the purpose of driving the saw. As early as the fourteenth century, mills were erected for the operation of mechanical saws driven by water wheels. Since these power-driven mills adversely affected the livelihood of the sawyers who operated hand-saw mills, the people rebelled against their use and, in many cases, entire mills were destroyed. The use of power saws was so objectionable in England at one time that Parliament enacted a law prohibiting their construction. General Bentham took out the first patent in England for a saw powered by steam in 1793.

In setting up a home workshop one hundred years ago, one might have chosen a circular saw similar to the one illustrated in Fig. 1-3. The "high speed" necessary for the operation of this saw was obtained by pumping the foot treadle which set in motion the large flywheel. There is indication that this saw was used mostly for ripping and rabbeting stock of less than $1\frac{1}{2}''$ in thickness. Adjustment for the depth of cut was

FIG. 1-3   Amateur's circular sawing machine. (From an advertisement dated about 1850.)

obtained through the adjusting screw at the front of the machine. The table of the machine was hinged at the rear, and there was no provision for tilting the table to obtain angular cuts. This saw was sold on the market for the equivalent of $30.00 in England in the middle of the last century.

Many improvements, of course, have been made since the time of this treadle machine. Power engineering and improved materials have made possible an increase of speed from a few hundred revolutions per minute used in the treadle machine to 5000 revolutions per minute, available on some 8″ diameter circular saws today.

II

The Home-Workshop Circular Saw

A circular saw suitable for the home workshop may be either a bench or floor model. If one wants a large, rigid machine, he should consider a floor model. The more reasonably priced table or bench models can be fitted to a bench or stand which, in some cases, is available as an accessory. For those who wish to build their own stand, plans have been included on page 72. This stand or bench for the machine is a "must" for efficient use of the bench saw and should be one of the first projects constructed after the purchase of the saw.

The second main consideration in the selection of a machine is the size of the saw blade. The diameter of the blade on a circular saw is a good indication of the proportional size of the other major elements in the machine. Probably an 8″ diameter saw is the most popular size. A machine with this size of blade will rip a board $2\frac{1}{2}$″ in thickness, which is a satisfactory capacity for the type of work generally done in a small shop. With smaller diameter saws, the work that can be done is more limited. Saws less than 7″ in diameter are generally too limited in their capacity and so lightly constructed throughout that accurate work cannot be expected from their use. There is also a safety hazard in using some of the very cheap machines on the market, since several necessary adjusting and locking devices may be omitted in their construction.

Ten-inch saws, besides having larger capacity and being built to more rigid specifications, require a large motor to drive the saw. (See table on p. 12.) The size of the motor required for a 10″ saw may demand more current than the average fuse can carry. Installation of such a machine may necessitate expensive alterations in your present electrical wiring.

The size of the saw arbor and the type of bearings are next in importance in the selection of a saw. Seven-inch and 8″ saws are generally supplied with an arbor which will take a saw of either $\frac{1}{2}$″ or $\frac{5}{8}$″ bore. The $\frac{5}{8}$″ arbor is more often found in better machines, since this extra size insures smoother operation of the saw blade. Similarly, the 10″ machine is usually available with either a $\frac{5}{8}$″ or $\frac{3}{4}$″ arbor. Here again the smaller-sized arbor will give satisfactory service for the majority of work, but if one wishes a rigid, vibration-free machine, the one with the larger arbor should be chosen.

Bearings for the saw arbor may be of the split type, either bronze or babbit. Bronze is considered the better of the two bearing materials because it will stand up well under higher speeds. Be sure there is a provision for oiling these bearings

4

and also a method of "taking up" the bearing as it becomes worn. Grease-packed ball bearings which are permanently lubricated in the factory are superior to any other type of saw-arbor bearing. These bearings will give long service with little or no attention during the life of the machine.

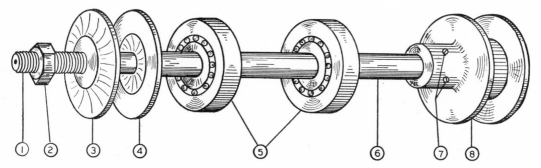

FIG. 2-1 A typical saw arbor. 1. Left-hand thread on the end of the arbor. 2. Nut for securing the saw to the arbor. (Turn the nut to the left to tighten.) 3. Outer flange, slides over the arbor freely. 4. Inner flange, fastened securely to the arbor. (Notice that the inner surface of both flanges is recessed.) 5. Bearings on which the arbor revolves. 6. Arbor or mandrel. 7. Set screws. (There should be two set screws in the hub of the pulley located 90 degrees apart for maximum holding power.) 8. V belt pulley.

Usually a "V" belt driving pulley (8) is mounted at one end of the saw arbor and fastened by means of a key and set screws (7). At the other end of the arbor the saw is secured in position between two steel flanges (3 & 4). The inside flange (4) should be fixed securely to the arbor, either pressed or shrunk in place and its face must run absolutely true. If this flange face has the slightest wobble, this defect is magnified in the running of the saw blade. The outside flange (3) should slide freely on the arbor over the threaded end. The arbor has a left-hand thread if the saw is mounted on the left end of the arbor. This left-hand thread is necessary so that the sawing process will tend to tighten the nut. If the saw is mounted

FIG. 2-2(a) Tilting table saw.

FIG. 2-2(b)   Tilting arbor saw.

on the right end of the arbor, the thread is right-handed for the same reason.

Most of the circular saws on the market are provided with either a means of tilting the table or the saw arbor for the purpose of producing certain bevel and angular cuts (Fig. 2-2). The tilting-arbor saw has the advantage of performing this angular sawing operation while the table remains horizontal. Saws with tilting tables are generally not as expensive as the tilting-arbor type. Although the tilting table is awkward to use, it will usually produce accurate bevel cuts. If the tilting arrangement is to be employed only occasionally, a tilting-table saw is not a handicap. However, if a variety of work is being contemplated, the extra money spent in purchasing a tilting-arbor saw will be well invested.

FIG. 2-3   Angular quadrant indicating angle of tilted arbor.

The mechanism which provides for this tilting operation should be rigidly constructed and there should be some provision for locking the adjustment securely at the desired angle. The more expensive saws have a large hand wheel on the side which, when turned, tilts either the table or the arbor through the action of a worm and worm wheel. This type of adjustment provides for an accurate setting, which is indicated on an angular quadrant at the front of the machine (Fig. 2-3). Machines which are tilted without the use of a mechanism and are merely locked by tightening a small bolt or clamp are neither safe nor satisfactory.

Some saws are made so that the table or saw arbor tilts away from the fence. This leaves more room between the rip fence and the saw when beveling narrow strips. The weight of long overhanging pieces being beveled will often cause the piece to "jerk up" and "kick back" as the cut is being finished on saws which tilt toward the fence. The safety factor of this feature should be an important consideration.

Every saw has some means of regulating the height of the blade above the table for cutting pieces of various thicknesses. Either the table is raised and lowered while the saw arbor remains stationary or the saw arbor is moved up and down while the table remains stationary. Generally machines with stationary tables are more rigidly constructed. A hand wheel conveniently located for this adjustment usually operates adjusting screws which can be easily locked at any height. Tables which are adjusted to height merely by means of small thumbscrews are unsafe and are not recommended.

The table of the saw should be provided with a slotted aluminum or wooden insert through which the saw projects. This insert does not provide enough of an opening for such accessories as the dado head or molding cutter. If you anticipate working with these accessories, inquire whether the manufacturer can supply table inserts with wide throats.

A well-constructed rip fence and cross-cut guide are necessary for accurate work. A rip fence which is as long as the table and is held in place by a clamping device at the front and rear of the table is usually preferred. A good type has one lever movement which will lock the fence both at the front and the rear. Be sure there is a means of adjustment on the fence so that the alignment can be corrected whenever necessary. A fence with a fine adjustment mechanism is desirable for accurate work. The cross-cut guide should also be accurately machined. The guide should be wide and sturdy enough to guide heavy work accurately.

Most home workshop machines are available with table extensions. If such extra equipment is not available, the saw is limited to its basic size, unless a home-made extension table is added. The new grill-type table extension gives unusually large working surface at low cost (see Fig. 3-1).

The availability of numerous accessories which are described in the following sections of this book is also a factor to consider when purchasing the original unit. Some accessories may seem rather specialized when you are first setting up your shop; however, as you progress in your work, you will find it helpful to have additional accessories available for special jobs.

Combination machines which include as many as five or six units in one are becoming more popular with the home mechanic who only has occasional time to spend in making or repairing jobs around the home. These home workshop units are generally limited in the size of work they can conveniently handle and are quite often overrated. The inconvenience of having to change over from one unit to another during a job, coupled with the fact that there is usually a sacrifice in rigid construction standards, makes this type of a combination machine less desirable than the conventional kind. However, if you have but little working space and expect to use the unit only occasionally, a machine of the above type may be the wisest choice.

III

Basic Tools and Accessories: Their Uses and Care

Circular saws are delivered with certain accessories as standard equipment (Fig. 3-1). A ripping fence, a cut-off guide, a saw guard, a set of maintenance tools, and a saw blade are usually provided with each purchase. The motor is generally not included in the list price because requirements differ somewhat with respect to the type and power of motor used.

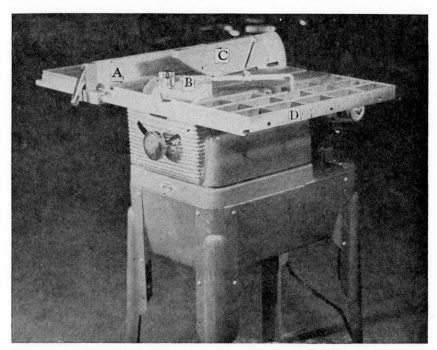

FIG. 3-1   Typical circular saw with accessories. (A) Ripping fence. (B) Cut-off guide and stop-rod. (C) Saw guard and splitter. (D) Table extension.

The Ripping Fence (or Guide). This accessory (*A* in Fig. 3-1) is used to guide the piece of wood as it is pushed into the saw when ripping (sawing with the grain). The fence must be of sturdy construction. It is attached to the saw table in such a manner that the distance from the face of the fence to the saw blade is adjustable. It is important that the fence be rigid so that it will maintain a position parallel to the saw blade during the ripping process.

9

There are several methods of attaching the fence to the saw table. One common method is to have it extend the entire length of the table and fastened at both ends. The medium-priced home workshop saws have a mechanical adjustment for the fence. The more expensive table saws have a micrometer adjustment for accurate positioning. Many table saws have some sort of a built-in scale for quick approximate adjustment of the saw-to-fence distance. A fence-tilting device is sometimes provided for angular ripping and beveling. Usually an adjusting mechanism is provided so that the fence may be brought to a position exactly parallel with the face of the saw.

The Cut-off Guide (or Gauge) and Stop-rod. When cross-cutting or making angular cuts, the work piece is held against the cut-off guide (*B* in Fig. 3-1). The guide is composed of a head and guide strip which is free to slide on the table in such a manner that the piece to be cut is held at a right angle or at any other desired angle to the face of the saw. It is common practice to pivot the head on a rectangular bar which slides in a slot in the saw table. The cut-off gauge is usually provided with a stop-rod. The end of this rod may be fastened in a hole or slot in the edge of the guide and is adjustable so that its bent end or stop-collar will hold a piece to be cut off at a specified distance from the saw. Its greatest use is for cutting off two or more pieces to the same length.

The Saw Guard and Safety Attachments. The saw guard (*C* in Fig. 3-1) is usually a box-like aluminum casting held in position over the saw blade in such a manner that it helps prevent the operator's hands from coming into contact with the saw. It also protects the operator from flying chips and sawdust. It is sometimes pivoted so that it automatically raises itself as the wood is fed to the saw and then drops over the blade as the sawing operation is completed. The guard must be adjusted so that it will never come in contact with the revolving blade.

Some saw guards incorporate a device known as a splitter. In the ripping process there is a tendency for the two pieces of wood beyond the saw to bend inward and bind the saw. The splitter is attached firmly to the saw table in back of the saw blade to help prevent the saw kerf from closing. Sometimes the saw guard is attached to the splitter. It is obvious that the splitter must be carefully lined up with the saw so that it will not interfere with the normal ripping process.

There is always some chance that the saw will cause the wood to kick back toward the operator. This action may be very dangerous, particularly when small, light pieces are being ripped. Sometimes the piece is propelled backward at a high velocity and could cause serious injury to the operator. To help prevent this action, a device known as an "anti-kickback" may be provided. Cogs or teeth on pivoted metal strips lock into the piece being ripped if it kicks back toward the operator.

Information About Circular Saw Blades. The saws for the table saw should be stored in such a manner that the teeth will not come into contact with anything that will dull them. Also be sure to guard against accidentally coming into contact with the teeth. If the saw is to be stored for an extended period, a thin film of oil will prevent rusting. Do not allow pitch or hard gummy deposits to remain on the saw. Remove them with turpentine or any other suitable solvent.

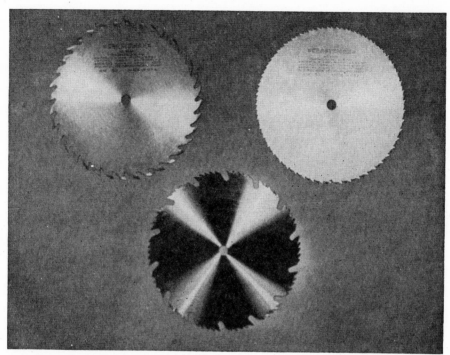

FIG. 3-2   Circular saw blades. *Upper left:* Rip; *Upper right:* Cross-cut; *Bottom:* combination.

Fundamentally there are three types of circular saw blades, those for rip-sawing, those for cross-cutting, and those which are combination saws for both ripping and cross-cutting (Fig. 3-2). The rip saw has chisel-like teeth (Fig. 3-3b) designed to cut smoothly when sawing parallel with the grain of the wood. The cross-cut or cut-off saw (Fig. 3-3a) has pointed teeth similar to knife blades which

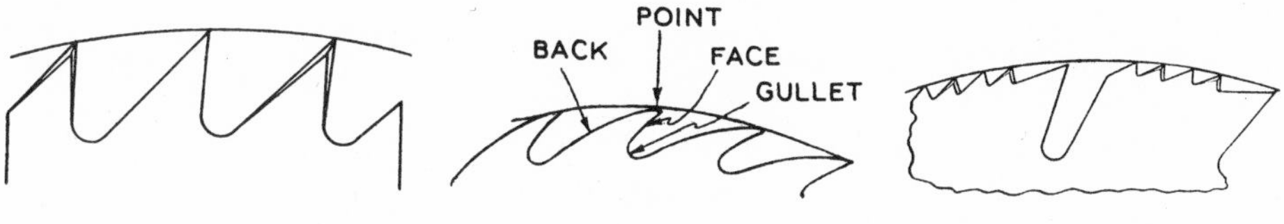

POINT

BACK | FACE

GULLET

(a) CROSS CUT SAW TEETH   (b) RIP SAW TEETH   (c) COMBINATION SAW TEETH

FIG. 3-3   Circular saw tooth shapes.

cut easily across the grain. The combination saw (Fig. 3-3c) is, as the name implies, fitted with a combination of the two kinds of teeth in order that both ripping and cross-cutting may be done. In selecting and using a saw of any of the above types there are certain factors which must be kept in mind.

1. Be sure that the center hole of the saw blade fits the arbor accurately. This is very important. Any looseness will cause excessive vibration, dangerous operation, and a poor cutting saw.

HELPFUL INFORMATION ABOUT CIRCULAR SAWS

Diameter of Blade	Standard Center Hole Sizes	No. of Teeth			Gauge	Rpm*	Approx. Depth Cut.	Motor H.P.
		Rip	Cross-cut	Comb.				
6″	$\frac{1}{2}, \frac{5}{8}, \frac{3}{4}$	40	100–120	40	18	6350	$1\frac{1}{2}$	$\frac{1}{4}$–$\frac{1}{2}$
7″	$\frac{1}{2}, \frac{5}{8}, \frac{3}{4}$	36	100–120	40	18	5450	$1\frac{3}{4}$	$\frac{1}{3}$–$\frac{1}{2}$
8″	$\frac{1}{2}, \frac{5}{8}, \frac{3}{4}, \frac{7}{8}$	36	100–150	40	18	4600	2	$\frac{1}{2}$–$\frac{3}{4}$
10″	$\frac{5}{8}, \frac{3}{4}, 1$	30, 36	100–150	40	16	3920	3	$\frac{3}{4}$–1
12″	$\frac{3}{4}, 1$	30, 36	100–150	40	14	3260	4	1–2
14″	$1, 1\frac{1}{2}$	30, 36	100–170	44	14	2750	5	2–5

* Computed for a rim speed of 10,000 ft. per min.

2. Run the saw at the correct peripheral speed (rim speed expressed in feet per minute). A rule of thumb for computing the peripheral speed is as follows: Divide the diameter of saw (expressed in inches) by 4. Then multiply by the speed of the arbor shaft (rpm). For example, suppose a 1750-rpm motor were to be connected directly to a saw arbor carrying an 8″ saw. The peripheral speed would then be $\frac{8}{4} \times 1750$, or 3500 feet per minute. Consequently, it may be seen that the common 1750-rpm motor does not revolve fast enough to allow a direct connection to the saw arbor if an 8″ saw is used. In order to utilize the above motor a set of pulleys must be installed to obtain at least a 3 to 1 increase in saw speed. Let us suppose that a 6″ diameter pulley were used on the motor shaft. In order to obtain the necessary pulley ratio, a 2″ pulley could then be used on the arbor shaft. The connecting belt between the motor pulley and the arbor pulley would cause the arbor to turn at 5250 rpm ($1750 \times \frac{6}{2}$). Applying the above rule for an 8″ saw will give a peripheral speed of 10,500 feet per minute, ($\frac{8}{4} \times 5250$), which is within the limits of acceptable saw speeds. The table above lists speeds and additional useful information about circular saws.

3. Keep the saw sharp at all times. When a saw blade is manufactured, it is made with a certain amount of internal stress called saw tension, which helps to keep it running true at the required high speed. When this tension is disturbed by heating or excessive straining, the saw no longer runs true and must be re-tensioned. Only a saw-conditioning expert can perform the retensioning process. Time spent in keeping saws properly conditioned will always pay good dividends in obtaining accurate, smooth and efficient saw table work. A detailed description of saws and the art of saw conditioning follows:

Reconditioning Circular Saw Blades. A good cutting saw must have sharp teeth which run true. To make the teeth run true, the saw blade must fit the arbor and all teeth must be of equal height. Also the cutting edge of teeth must remove enough stock so that the blade below the teeth will not bind. To accomplish this last condition, the teeth are sometimes alternately "set" over to left and right (Fig. 3-4a). Another method is to provide an adequate amount of blade taper from thin, near the arbor, to thick at the teeth. A blade having this taper is called "hollow ground" (Fig. 3-4b). Another requisite for a fast cutting saw is correctly shaped "throats" or "gullets" in front of the saw teeth to provide sawdust space (Fig. 3-4c).

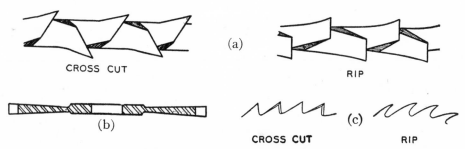

FIG. 3-4 (a) "Set" in cross-cut and rip saws. (b) Cross section of hollow-ground blade. (c) Showing difference in gullets.

In the process of reconditioning, the saw blade is brought back as nearly as possible to its original specifications. In general, there are four definite steps which are necessary in reconditioning a saw blade:

1. Jointing to make the teeth all of equal length.

2. Setting to give clearance. (Hollow ground saws require no setting.)

3. Sharpening the teeth by filing or grinding them.

4. Gumming (shaping) the gullets to provide sawdust clearance.

Jointing. This process is done to make all the teeth of equal height. It must be done while the saw is correctly mounted on the arbor. It is advisable to remove the saw and inspect and clean both the saw and the arbor and then remount before jointing the blade.

To remove the saw, loosen the arbor nut. Remove the table insert and hold a block of wood as in Fig. 3-5 so that the saw teeth will be pulled downward into

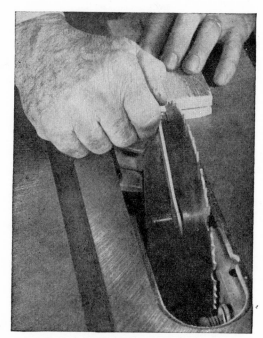

FIG. 3-5 Removing the circular saw blade.

the block when the wrench loosens the nut. To loosen the nut, turn it in a direction the same as the normal operating direction.

After cleaning the arbor and saw, test to make sure that the saw fits the arbor snugly. It is good practice to mark the saw and the arbor (usually on the fixed flange) in some manner so that the blade may be returned to exactly the same position each time it is remounted. This is important because it is practically impossible to make the saw fit the arbor perfectly. Consequently, the saw is more likely to run smoothly if returned to the position in which it is jointed.

The process of jointing is carried out in the following steps. Lower the saw blade until the teeth barely protrude above the table. Check this with a piece of wood while the blade is turning, making sure the teeth just touch the wood. Hold a piece of abrasive stone flat on the table and push it slowly and firmly across the teeth (Fig. 3-6). *Caution:* This is a dangerous operation if incorrectly

(a)

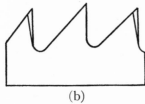

(b)

Fig. 3-6   (a) Jointing the circular blade.
(b) All teeth must be the same height.

performed. In any case it is good practice to wear goggles during this process. This action will cause a small amount of steel to be removed from the longest teeth. Stop the saw and examine the teeth. If each tooth has been touched by the abrasive stone, then jointing is complete. If all the teeth have not been touched, then the saw must be slightly raised and the process repeated. Do not remove any more steel than is necessary to make the saw blade concentric. When the process is completed, all teeth will be the same height (Fig. 3-6b).

Setting. The saw must be removed from the arbor for the setting process. Before the blade is removed, it should be inspected to determine if it needs gumming, or shaping of the gullets. Gumming is usually necessary after about

8 to 12 filings in order to maintain the correct shape of teeth and gullets. If gumming is necessary, hold a pencil against the saw while turning it by hand to obtain a circle which will mark the bottom of the gullets when they are correctly filed. The actual gumming process can be done simultaneously with the filing of the teeth or as a separate process, depending upon the type of saw being filed.

After the saw has been removed from the arbor, the teeth are set by bending the points alternately left and right a speci-

FIG. 3-7   Commercial setting device.

fied amount. For rip and cross-cut saws, set every second tooth on one side and then reverse the saw and set the remaining teeth on the other side. (See Fig. 3-4a.) All the teeth must be set by the same amount so that the saw, when used, will not have a tendency to "run" to left or right and so that each tooth will do the same amount of cutting.

There are several inexpensive setting devices which may be purchased (Fig. 3-7). Essentially they consist of a stand to position the saw teeth over a beveled anvil. The teeth are bent by means of a

FIG. 3-8   Tooth in position for setting.

punch (Figs. 3-8, 3-9). The set portion of the teeth should not be more than $\frac{1}{3}$ the total height of the tooth (Fig. 3-10). The angle of a set when sawing kiln-dried wood should be about 5°. Too much set produces saw chatter or vibration which results in a rough cut.

Fɪɢ. 3-9   Tooth after being struck by punch.

Sharpening. During the sharpening process the saw must be held in some sort of a clamp, so that the teeth will be well supported. Commercial types are available (Fig. 3-11). A serviceable clamp to hold in a bench vise may be constructed at home as illustrated in Fig. 3-12. (Refer to Project No. 7.) Most craftsmen feel that it is not advisable to try filing the saw blade while it is mounted on the

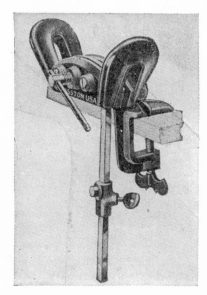

arbor. For slight touching-up, this may be done, but, in general, the saw blade should be removed and held in a suitable clamp. The sharpening operation must result in obtaining the correct tooth shape.

Reconditioning a Rip Saw. Rip saws have teeth shaped so that they chisel their way through the wood (Fig. 3-4a). They are usually filed straight

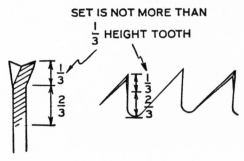

SET IS NOT MORE THAN
$\frac{1}{3}$ HEIGHT TOOTH

Fɪɢ. 3-10

Fɪɢ. 3-11   Commercial type saw-filing clamp.

across at right angles to the blade with the proper amount of "hook." A line along the face or front of the tooth if continued would pass about half-way between the center of the hole in the saw and the tooth line (Fig. 3-13). This angle is important and is called "the angle of the hook." A saw tooth having this amount of hook is common practice and is referred to as a "$\frac{1}{4}$ hook tooth" because the intersection of the hook-line is at a point $\frac{1}{4}$ of the diameter of the saw from the axis.

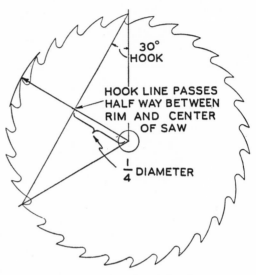

Fig. 3-12   Home-made saw clamp.

Fig. 3-13   Tooth hook.

When filing rip saws, the file must be held at right angles to the blade, with the face of the file against the face of the tooth (Fig. 3-14). A 6″ to 8″ mill file with two round edges is often used so that both the tooth face and the gullet may be formed with the file at the same time. If much metal is to be removed to bring

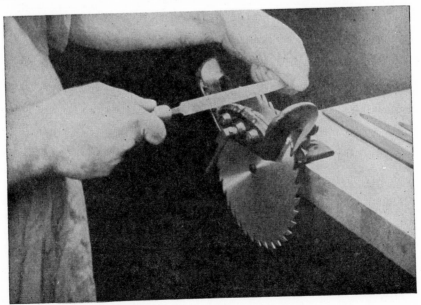

Fig. 3-14   Filing a rip saw.

the jointed teeth to the necessary sharp point, then a bastard (rough-cut) file is used. For the last few strokes, a finer cut file (second-cut or smooth) will produce a sharper and smoother cutting edge on the teeth. File the teeth that are set away from you first, then reverse the saw and file the remaining teeth. Be sure not to file the teeth too much. The face of the teeth should be filed just enough to remove the dulled portion and bring the face surface back to the jointed area (Fig. 3-15).

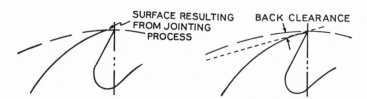

FIG. 3-15   (a) Before filing back clearance. (b) After filing back and face clearance.

After the face has been finished, then the back of the tooth must be filed to produce clearance back of the cutting edge (Fig. 3-15b). Some rip saws are filed with the cutting edge not straight across the blade, but at an angle on alternate teeth. This tooth shape has resulted from a desire to combine rip-saw action with cross-cut action (Fig. 3-16). Actually this type of saw can be classed as a combination saw. Be sure to inspect your saw blade before you file it and bring the tooth shape to the original type.

If you do not have a round-edge file, the gumming may be done with a rat-tail file. Usually a few strokes in the gullet of each tooth when the saw is filed will be enough to retain the original shape of the teeth (Fig. 3-17). In filing saws, the tooth shape is of prime importance, and to retain the correct shape it may be necessary to take a few extra file strokes off the face of the back of the teeth. A shop "kink" that may be used by beginners is to drill a small hole in the file handle and insert a piece of wire as shown in Fig. 3-18. If the hole is correctly positioned so that the wire is vertical when the file is in the proper filing position, then

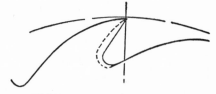

FRONT LINE ANGLE CHANGED

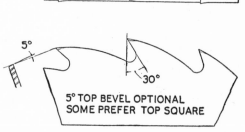

5°

30°

5° TOP BEVEL OPTIONAL
SOME PREFER TOP SQUARE

FIG. 3-16   Rip saw with slight top bevel.

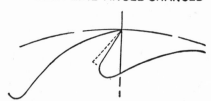

FIG. 3-17   Do not distort gullets. Distortion will cause cracks and breaks.

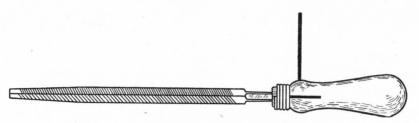

Fɪɢ. 3-18   Wire in handle to help prevent the "roll."

much more uniformly shaped teeth should result. This trick helps to eliminate a filing action common to beginners called file "roll."

Reconditioning a Cross-cut Saw. Cross-cut saws are reconditioned with much the same procedure as that used for rip saws. The saw is jointed and set as before, but the filing process is somewhat differ-

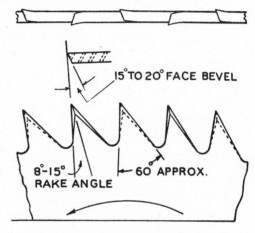

ent. The filing is done with a 6″ to 8″ slim taper file. In this case the gullet of the tooth is shaped while sharpening the teeth, thus eliminating the step called gumming. The teeth are smaller and are beveled about 15° on both the face and the back (Fig. 3-19). Notice that the filed surfaces of the tooth are always on the side away from the set, thus producing the sharp cutting points on the outside of the saw. When filing, the original bevels should be maintained and the file must be held at the correct angle with the blade to produce these

Fɪɢ. 3-19   Cross-cut teeth detail.

bevels. The rake angle varies from about 8° to 15° and the included angle of the tooth point is approximately 60° (Fig. 3-19). As in the case of the rip saw, the alternate teeth that are set away from you are filed first. Then the saw is reversed and the remaining teeth filed. Figure 3-20 shows the approximate position

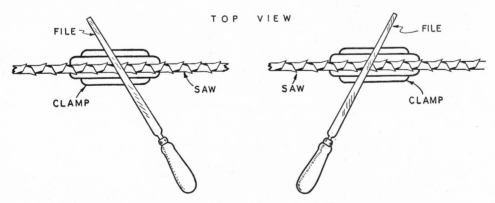

Fɪɢ. 3-20   Approximate file positions when filing cross-cut saws.

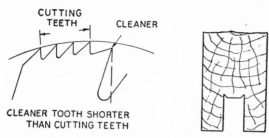

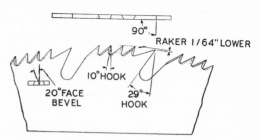

FIG. 3-21 (a) Combination saw teeth. (b) Saw kerf made by combination saws.

FIG. 3-22 Specifications for a typical saw tooth.

of the file for the above procedure. Be sure that you study the tooth shape before you start filing and that you position the file to maintain the correct angles. Remember that the teeth must all be the same shape and height after the filing process is completed.

Reconditioning a Combination Saw. When reconditioning the combination saw, both the rip saw and the cross-cut saw procedures must be used. Figure 3-21a shows the teeth on a typical combination saw. The cutting teeth cut the wood fibers on each side and then the raker or cleaner tooth behind them advances and cleans out the center of the cut. The cutting action of the teeth is shown in Fig. 3-21b. After jointing and setting (hollow-ground saw requires no set), the raker teeth are filed. The raker tooth is similar to the rip-saw tooth, but it is filed from $\frac{1}{64}''$ to $\frac{1}{32}''$ below the height of the other teeth. The cutting teeth are filed next. They are sharpened like cross-cut teeth. Figure 3-22 shows specifications for a common combination saw. The jointing process will leave a slight rounded surface on the teeth. Be sure to file only enough to bring the teeth to a point. File the gullets to their original round shape.

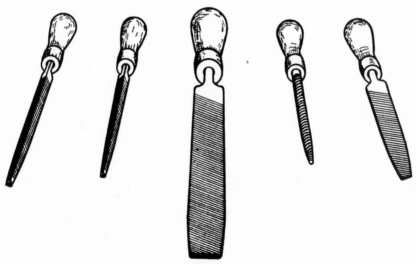

FIG. 3-23 Common files for sharpening circular saw. Left to right 8 inch regular taper, 7 inch slim taper, 10 inch round edge mill, 7 inch rat tail and 8 inch 2nd cut mill.

Figure 3-23 illustrates the files commonly used in the sharpening process.

Dressing a Circular Saw. The filing process will usually leave the cutting points slightly out of line. This is true because all the teeth cannot be set exactly the same and it is impossible to file all teeth exactly the same. The dressing process will bring all the cutting points into line and thus greatly improve the smooth cutting action.

The procedure is as follows: Mount the saw securely on the arbor, making sure that the saw and arbor are clean. Check the saw and arbor marks to make certain the saw is mounted in the correct position. Raise the saw until it protrudes to its maximum height above the table. Now start the saw and hold an abrasive stone with its flat side on the table and its edge against the blade back of the teeth set. Draw the stone very slowly toward the teeth until the set portion is reached as in Fig. 3-24. Only a very slight amount of contact is needed to bring the teeth into line. Repeat on the other side of the saw.

FIG. 3-24
Dressing a rip saw to make it cut smoothly.

Dado Head. This is a very handy accessory for making grooves (or dadoes). It replaces the common saw on the arbor and in action is nothing but a **thick** saw. Its principal advantage is that a relatively wide groove can be made with one pass. It consists of two outside blades and a set of inside chipper blades (Fig. 3-25). The outside blades are often $\frac{1}{8}''$ thick and the chipper blades come in $\frac{1}{16}''$, $\frac{1}{8}''$ and $\frac{1}{4}''$ thicknesses. Also paper washers are supplied to make the fractional adjustments which are often necessary in obtaining a good fit for a grooved joint. In operation the dado head is used much like the conventional circular saw. However, it should be noted that a special table insert is necessary and that some caution must be observed because of the much larger bite that the dado head takes in the work piece. The saw guard and splitter along with the "anti-kickbacks" must be removed. Consequently, the operation is necessarily more dangerous.

In setting up the dado head, space the swaged ends of the chipper blades as evenly as possible around the circumference (Fig. 3-26). Be sure to test the final

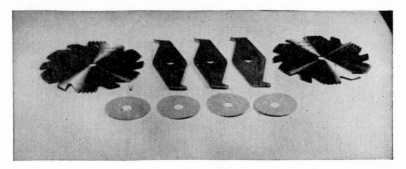

FIG. 3-25   Typical dado head parts.

setup with a test piece before making a cut in the work piece. The dado cutting points must be kept sharp. A dull dado head is extremely dangerous to use.

FIG. 3-26   Proper position for inside cutters.

Tenoning Attachment. The tenoning attachment (Fig. 3-27) is used to support the work piece when cutting a tenon. Its primary advantage is that of holding the piece exactly perpendicular to the table while making the cheek cuts on tenons. It consists of an adjustable clamping device mounted on a guide strip which runs in the table groove. It is used to advantage when many identical tenons are to be cut, but is hardly worth buying to cut just an occasional tenon.

Molding Head. Many different designs for molding can be cut by utilizing a molding head in place of the circular saw. The head may be purchased with a variety of cutters (Fig. 3-28). Many interesting and practical designs for molding are made by combining a succession of cuts by two or more cutters. It is necessary to use a special wide throat table insert, and it is imperative that the molding be well supported as it is being cut.

Wobble Washers. Grooves and dadoes may be cut in one pass when the circular saw is mounted on the arbor at an angle. To accomplish this, two split beveled washers called wobble washers are used (Fig. 3-29). These washers may be ad-

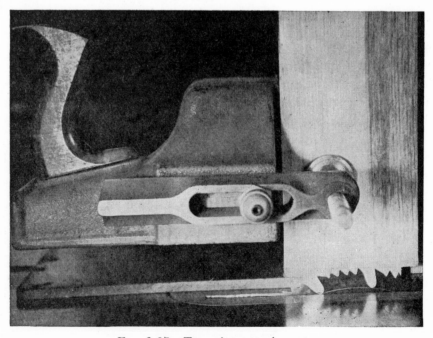

FIG. 3-27   Tenoning attachment.

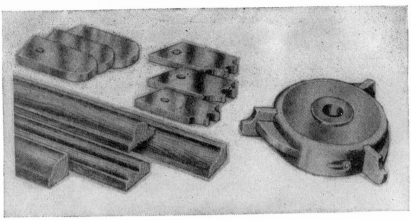

Fig. 3-28   Typical molding head with cutters.

justed to the required amount of bevel and then the saw, with a washer on each side, is mounted on the arbor. When the saw is rotated, it wobbles and the saw cuts a wide kerf (Fig. 3-30). The practical limit of wobble for small saws (8″ or 10″) is something less than $\frac{3}{4}$″.

Clamp Attachment for the Cross-cut Guide. This accessory provides a means of holding the work piece while it is being pushed into a saw with the cross-cut guide. It is particularly advantageous when the work piece is short and when mitering is being done. It consists of a bar with adjustable clamps, one end of which is mounted on the guide head and the other on the slide bar (Fig. 3-31).

Special Saws and Abrasive Wheels. There are some special-purpose saws available. The saw shown in Fig. 3-32 has been especially designed so that it will cut through nails and small screws without excessive dulling. The saw illustrated in Fig. 3-33 has been designed to combine smooth cutting action with maximum safety.

One of the big advantages claimed for this saw is its "anti-kickback" feature. It seems reasonable that such a saw with only a fraction of the normal teeth will dull much more quickly than the normal type. However, it certainly is more

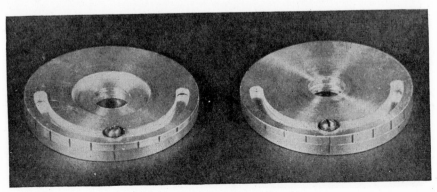

Fig. 3-29   Wobble washers.

quickly and easily sharpened. Saws of this type should fill a long-felt need in certain applications.

Abrasive wheels designed to cut metal, plastics, glass, stone, and other materials are available (Fig. 3-34). They are thin disks of strongly bonded abrasive, and each wheel is designed to do a certain class of jobs. Be sure to consult the

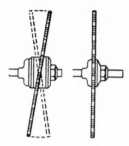

manufacturer's specifications to obtain good results. These wheels replace the conventional saw blade and are used much the same except that the rate of feed is slower. If possible, use the saw guard and be sure to wear goggles. It is good practice to hold round or irregular pieces in some sort of a jig during the cutting process. Most of the wheels are run dry and at the normal saw speed. After continued use, the wheel should be dressed, with a grinding wheel type dresser, to maintain clean and true edges.

FIG. 3-30 Wobble saw and normal saw position.

The Feather Board. The feather board is an accessory used to hold a work piece against the fence while ripping and to help prevent kickback. (See also Project 2.) It consists of a board from 3″ to 5″ wide with lateral cuts to make narrow strips at one end (Fig. 3-35). The ends of the narrow strips are cut off at about a 45° angle. The board is then clamped to the table in the position shown. The piece being ripped may slide in a forward direction by the ends of the strips, and the elasticity of the strips will provide a definite and positive force which holds the work piece against the rip fence. If the work piece tends to move backward, then the strips bind and resist this motion.

FIG. 3-31 Clamp attachment for the cross-cut guide.

FIG. 3-32   Nail cutting saw.

FIG. 3-33   P.T.I. blade.

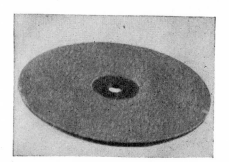

FIG. 3-34   Abrasive wheel.

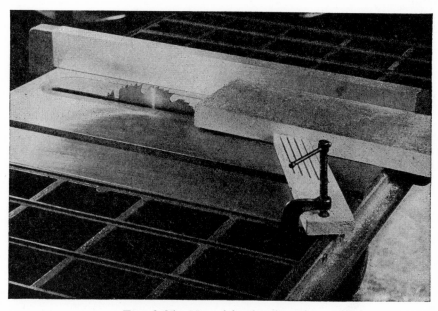

FIG. 3-35   Use of feather board.

FIG. 3-36   Typical pusher stick.

Removable Bushings. It is sometimes necessary to use a saw whose center hole is larger than the arbor upon which it is to be run. Bushings to provide a smaller center hole are available. The common sizes are: $\frac{3}{4}''$ to $\frac{5}{8}''$, $\frac{3}{4}''$ to $\frac{1}{2}''$, $\frac{5}{8}''$ to $\frac{1}{2}''$.

Pusher Stick. When ripping narrow strips it is necessary to push the work piece past the saw at dangerously close quarters. In this case it is good practice to use a specially shaped stick such as the one illustrated in Fig. 3-36. It is called a pusher stick and should be used whenever the ripping process would otherwise bring the fingers dangerously close to the saw. (See also Project 1.)

IV

Basic Operations

When using the circular saw, you should observe the following conditions:
1. That it is well lubricated
2. That the guards are in place
3. That it is clean
4. That the floor is not congested where you are standing
5. That you are standing firmly on both feet in a comfortable position, feet apart, with freedom of movement in all directions, and not directly in line with the saw. You should wear no loose clothing and should not engage in conversation with another person during the time you are operating the machine.

6. If the saw has been used by someone else before you, always rotate the saw blade by hand to see that everything is free before turning on the power. Check your saw to see that it is sharp.

Ripping. The most fundamental operation on the variety saw is ripping parallel with the grain (Fig. 4-1). It is common practice to set the saw for height, when

FIG. 4-1   Ripping with the grain.

ripping, so that it protrudes above the piece not more than $\frac{1}{4}''$ to $\frac{1}{2}''$. The reasons for this include, beside considerations of safety: a full arc of teeth will come in contact with the wood and will make a cleaner saw kerf; the saw will not tend to bind as much as it would if it were set to a greater height.

Perhaps the most fundamental kind of ripping is done when a board is edged by use of a guide line. It requires practice to do this job well. The board must be run straight, and it must be sawed with the kerf on the waste side of the line, thus giving you maximum width of clear stock. If, when ripping to a line, your board gradually works away from the line, it should not be brought back abruptly. You must realign the work within the limits of the saw kerf you are cutting. Otherwise the back teeth of the saw, as they come up above the table, will catch the board and throw it toward you.

Before attempting this operation, be sure that you understand clearly the directions given. Try the operation first on short pieces that you can handle easily. If you do not care to rip by use of a guide line only, edge the board with a hand saw and joint it with your power jointer or jointing plane. Then make the next rip cut with the aid of the ripping fence. You will thus avoid risking the danger of kickback.

A valuable suggestion for ripping with the line is to place the board in its correct position in front of the saw with the guide line on the edge of the saw. Then by sighting along the line, you can place the board very nearly in its correct position with respect to the saw.

It is very difficult to rip a board to a line unless you stand directly behind the saw. This may sound inconsistent with the safety precautions previously given, but there seems to be no better way to insure an accurate cut.

After the board has had one work edge made, the board can be ripped to width by using the rip fence set at the right distance from the saw. Allow enough distance for the finished width of the board plus an allowance for finishing the sawed edge on the jointer or by hand. Place the working edge up against the rip fence and push the board by hand until your hand comes within a foot or so of the saw. Then use the pusher stick (Fig. 4-2). If you are ripping a long board, the sawed end of the board must be supported, either mechanically or with the help of another person.

Never reach over the saw to clear sawdust, chips, or shavings, or whatever may have collected there. Always use a stick for this purpose. Probably more accidents are caused by reaching over the saw to clear the table than by any other one reason.

When you are ripping a board on a saw, keep the board against the rip fence. It may be that the board will have a tendency to work away from the fence or cramp between the saw and fence, or pinch the saw. The first two conditions may be caused by failing to push the board in a straight line, by an improperly sharpened saw, or by a dull saw. These defective conditions must be avoided if

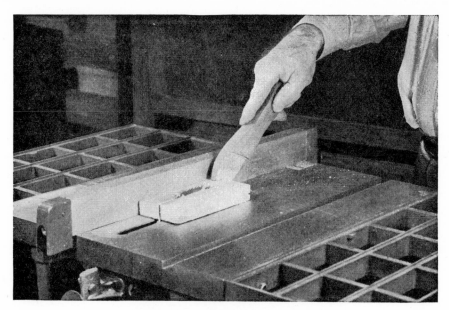

Fig. 4-2 Using the pusher stick.

satisfactory ripping is to be done. Push the board straight; keep it down on the table; and use the pusher stick when nearing the saw. If you have a helper, be sure that you and you alone do the feeding. The helper merely carries the weight of the board.

Many kinds of wood, when being sawed, have a tendency to close the saw kerf or pinch the saw. As a result, the board will either pinch the splitter or, if no splitter is back of the saw, the teeth of the saw. If the board does pinch, it will have a tendency to kick back because of the action of the saw teeth. This condition may be partially avoided by placing a wedge in the saw kerf to counteract the pinch. Another method of correcting this dangerous kickback is to hold the piece securely so that it cannot kick back, although sometimes it is better to lift the piece off the saw and start ripping on the other end. If you hold the piece down and allow it to continue to pinch the saw, the blade may become heated and, in extreme cases, will cause a change in temper and tension of the saw. It may also blow a fuse or burn out the motor.

For the beginner, a novelty or combination blade is the best type to use for short ripping and cutting off. It does not catch in the work; it makes a smooth cut and is easy to operate if it is kept sharp. The best type of novelty saw to use is the one that is hollow ground so that the teeth do not require setting. Be sure the teeth are kept sharp, however.

Cross-cutting. The next most fundamental operation on the saw is cross-cutting. This should always be done with the aid of the guide or gauge as it is sometimes called. Never try to cross-cut a long piece. Pieces over 5 or 6 feet long cannot be controlled easily. Pieces that can be easily held against the guide are

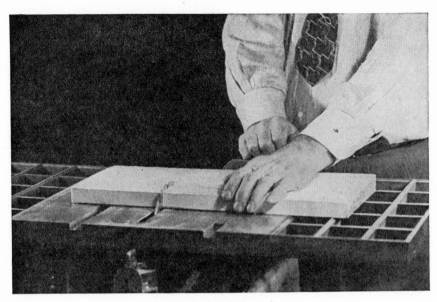

FIG. 4-3   Cross-cutting.

the only pieces that should be cross-cut (Fig. 4-3). *Caution:* Never use the rip
fence as a cut-off guide. Pieces will jam between the saw and fence, a condition
extremely dangerous to operator and machine.

To cut off at one end a board which has a working edge, place the board tightly
against the cut-off guide, use the right hand to push the guide, and use the left
hand to hold the piece against the guide (Fig. 4-3). It is usually good practice
when squaring stock to square the best end first. This will allow you to measure

FIG. 4-4   Use of the stop block.

from the best portion of the stock so that any remaining part sawed off will be from the inferior end of the wood.

Place the saw against the mark at which the board is to be cut. Be sure the cutting mark is on the correct side of the saw. Push the board straight across the table until you have finished the cut. The rip fence must not be near the piece that has been sawed off because if piece touches the rip fence and the saw at the same time, it may jam between the two.

When cross-cutting several pieces to length, the stop-rod gauge is used for long pieces and the stop block is used for short pieces. When using the stop block (Fig. 4-4), it is necessary to guide the piece by the use of the cut-off guide. It is good practice to avoid sawing short pieces which do not allow an adequate length to be held against the guide. If an adequate length is not held against the guide, the piece may bind against the stop block and tilt on the saw, possibly causing an accident.

The stop-rod gauge may be used for cutting long pieces to length after all the pieces have been squared on one end. Place the squared end against the stop-rod gauge and, holding the piece against the cut-off guide as described before, push the piece by the saw (Fig. 4-5). *Caution:* It must be carefully noted that, after this piece has been sawed off, its position is between the stop-rod gauge and the saw. The next motion must be either to push the piece completely by the saw or, while holding the piece tightly against the gauge, to pull it back to the front of the table away from the saw. If this caution is not observed, the piece may cramp against the saw and cause injury to the operator or the work piece.

FIG. 4-5   Use of the stop-rod gauge.

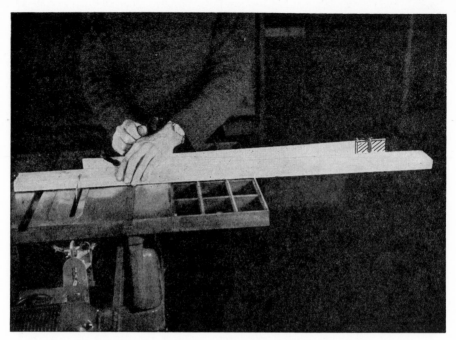

FIG. 4-6   Home-made gauge for sawing long pieces.

A home-made gauge can be made for sawing long pieces to length by clamping a flexible wooden bar, approximately $\frac{1}{4}'' \times 2''$, to the cross-cut guide. On this bar is clamped a wooden stop. The flexibility of the bar allows you to complete both the operation of squaring a working end and then sawing to length without any change in adjustment of the setup (Fig. 4-6). *Note:* As before, it is always wise to have one sample piece for testing purposes.

Mitering or Angular Cutting. The next basic operation is mitering or angular cutting. Mitering usually refers to a 45-degree cut and is accomplished in much the same manner as cross-cutting except that the guide is set at an angle indicated on the quadrant. Figure 4-7 shows the guide set for 45-degree mitering. Note that the left hand which holds the work up against the guide is much nearer the saw than it would be for 90-degree cross-cutting. If, of course, the guide were set for the opposite 45-degree miter, the hand would be farther away. Both of these conditions should be carefully noted for safety reasons. The pressure brought to bear by the left hand should be at right angles to the face of the guide to avoid slippage of the work piece. Usually a 45-degree miter is the smallest angle that can be cut by the use of a cross-cut guide. Always have a test piece available when making your first angular cut. The first setting of the guide may not be accurate because this setting is a manual operation. Use the test piece until the proper setting is achieved. This will safeguard against ruining your work piece. This procedure applies to all angular cuts.

Compound Cuts. Compound angular or compound miter cuts are easily cut on the tilting table saw or tilting arbor saw. On the tilting table saw, the method is as

FIG. 4-7 Making a miter cut.

follows: Set the table at the angle that will give you the desired cut on the thickness of the piece. Set the cross-cut guide for the angle that will give you the desired cut on the width of the piece. These two angles together will give you the compound angular cut. Again it is wise to use a test piece to see if both settings are correct before cutting the work piece.

FIG. 4-8 Making a compound cut.

In making a compound cut on a tilting arbor saw, the tilting of the arbor will give you the angular cut on the thickness of the piece and the setting of the cross-cut guide will give you the angular cut on the width of the piece. Again use a test piece for a trial cut.

The method of cutting is indicated in Fig. 4-8. The pressure exerted by the left hand is always directly toward the surface of the cross-cut guide to avoid slippage of the work piece. If your saw table is one that does not have a cross-cut guide with a quadrant, or a tilting arbor or a tilting table, a temporary wooden tilting fence can be made and fastened to the right-angle fence and used as a guide for making these cuts. Also an angular piece can be placed against your cross-cut guide to give you the angle necessary for making the width cut of the compound cut.

Cutting Bevels and Chamfers on a Circular Saw. A bevel is an angular cut on the edge or end of a board. This differs from a chamfer which is also an angular cut but goes only partially across the edge or end of the board. The usual method of cutting bevels and chamfers on a circular saw is to use either the tilting arbor saw or the saw with the tilting table. (See Figs. 4-9 and 4-10). Cutting bevels by aid of the tilting fence is not as convenient as either of the other two methods and is not recommended.

When cutting a bevel with a tilting arbor saw, the work lays flat on the table and the saw is tilted. (See Fig. 4-9.) Usually there is a quadrant on the machine that will indicate the angle at which your saw is tilted. It is a good idea to check the angle by cutting a test piece to see whether or not your setting is correct.

FIG. 4-9   Sawing a bevel with the use of a tilting arbor saw.

In cutting a bevel or a chamfer on a tilting arbor saw, the procedure is as follows:

1. Set the saw by turning the hand wheel until the quadrant indicates the correct angle.

2. Set the fence the proper distance from the saw.

3. With the work laying flat on the table and guided by the rip fence, proceed to saw the bevel with the same caution that would be used in rip sawing. It is advisable to use a pusher stick.

Cutting Bevels by Use of a Tilting Table. Cutting bevels with the use of the tilting table is not a difficult operation (Fig. 4-10). The work piece is flat on the table and is guided by the rip fence. The rip fence is set to the proper distance

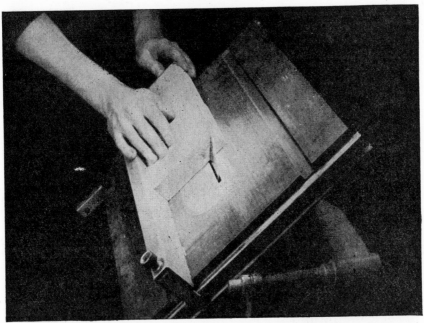

FIG. 4-10 Sawing a bevel with the use of a tilting table saw.

from the saw. Special care should be exercised as it will be noted that the work has a tendency to slide sideways down the table while the operation is being performed. This, of course, must be guarded against, as it might cause damage to the work piece or a dangerous kickback. Care also should be taken so that the piece is held firmly between the saw and the fence. It should not be lifted until after it has passed by the saw; otherwise it will jam and damage the material or injure the worker. A helper is very desirable in this operation; or sometimes you can clamp a piece on the table which will serve as a guide for the sawed portion.

Three of the necessary features that will aid in making a satisfactory bevel are: (1) a real sharp combination saw; (2) the setting of the fence to the proper distance; and (3) pushing the work in a straight line.

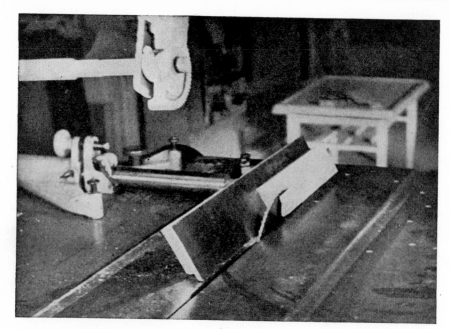

Fig. 4-11   Sawing a bevel with the use of a tilting fence.

In case it is absolutely necessary to cut a bevel with the aid of a tilting fence (Fig. 4-11), if it is a wide piece it is good practice to fasten a supporting board to the fence. The work piece can then rest against the support and still have the lower edge in contact with the saw. Thus a sharp bevel can be cut, and the board which is clamped to the fence will give support while the operation is being performed.

In Fig. 4-11 you will observe that it is impossible to make an angular cut on a

Fig. 4-12   The rip fence set for a rabbet.

piece at any appreciable distance from the edge of the piece. The limitation is the small clearance afforded by the tilting fence and the saw.

Usually the setting of the tilting fence is accomplished by measuring the angle with a properly set carpenter's bevel or by use of the combination bevel protractor. A template cut to the correct angle may be used as a gauge in setting the rip fence. The rip fence is convenient if one is making a chamfer on a recess panel.

Rabbeting. Rabbeting is a process of cutting out a section of wood from the edge or end of the work piece—for example, the section which is removed in a picture frame to receive the glass and picture. In rabbeting you must first remove the guard or splitter in order to make space for the work itself.

There are several ways to do rabbeting on the saw, depending upon the di-

FIG. 4-13   Making the second cut of the rabbet.

mensions of the rabbet. For example, if you wish to make a rabbet $\frac{1}{2}'' \times \frac{1}{2}''$ you set the rip fence $\frac{1}{2}''$ from the outside of the saw. This $\frac{1}{2}''$ includes the width of the saw (Fig. 4-12). Then set the height of the saw $\frac{1}{2}''$ above the table. Use a test piece to check the adjustments on the saw before making final cuts. Then rip the piece with its face flat on the table and an edge up against the rip fence. Now place the proper face against the rip fence with the edge on the table for the second cut (Fig. 4-13). In case the rabbet is of two different dimensions, you must make one cut, then make a second setting for the other cut. If you have many pieces to rabbet, it is, of course, advisable first to run all pieces through one setting and then make the necessary change in the setting for the second cut.

If you are rabbeting on the end of a piece, it may be advisable to use the cross-cut guide to assist in feeding the piece over the saw (Fig. 4-14).

Rabbets can also be cut by setting the saw the correct height above the table

FIG. 4-14   Rabbeting the end of a piece.

and making all cuts while the board is flat on the table. The fence is moved as many times as is necessary a distance equal to the width of the saw kerf. This is convenient in some cases, but if you have more than one piece, of course, it is not an efficient method. However, in very wide pieces, it might be more desirable to do the job by the second method rather than to stand the piece on edge. The choice of method will have to be guided by two things: First, the dimensions of the piece; and, second, the size of the rabbet.

Rabbeting may also be done by using one of the dado heads described in the use of the dado head.

Grooving. Grooving is the process of cutting out a section of the work piece on the edge or face, for example, the groove on flooring or siding. When the groove is across the grain, it is called a dado. When grooving is done parallel with the grain, it is called ploughing. There are three methods of grooving on the circular saw. One is by the use of the saw with repeated cuts as Fig. 4-15 indicates. Another is by use of the dado head. The third is by the use of wobble washers, sometimes called wobble sawing.

When grooving with the saw, it is usually good practice to saw the outside cuts first, before the waste material between the cuts is removed. The saw runs straighter when cutting the full width of the saw kerf than it does when making partial-width cuts. This is the reason for making the outside cuts before the waste material is removed. Always use a test piece to check measurements before making cuts on the work piece.

If you wish to cut grooves across the grain, the procedure is practically the

Fig. 4-15   Making a groove by the use of repeated cuts.

same as above, except that you can use the cross-cutting guide for holding the piece and the rip fence as a stop (Fig. 4-15). As stated above, it is absolutely necessary to use a test piece when making these cuts. When cutting a dado, if the piece is slightly warped, care must be taken to keep the piece flat when making the cuts. It may be difficult to do this, and it is much better to use flat stock, if possible.

Cutting Gains. A *gain* might be called a stop dado. Hinge gain is a special type gain which may go across the edge of the piece or it may be made on the flat surface of the piece. A hinge gain is a recess that is made to receive the leaf of the hinge. It must be deep enough to receive the hinge leaf plus whatever clearance is needed. This can be determined only by closing the hinge, measuring and allowing clearance enough so that the hinged piece will swing free. Hinge gains can be made by the use of the cut-off saw, using both the rip fence and the cut-off guide. By setting the cut-off saw above the table surface a distance equal to the depth of the gain, and by positioning the center of the gain on the highest point of the saw, you can begin to position the cut-off guide.

The length of the gain should be laid out with a knife or pencil on the piece. The rip fence may be used as a stop guide at one end and the stop gauge can be used as a stop guide on the other end. In Fig. 4-16 a cut has been used to indicate the end of the gain. Fig. 4-16 also shows how the work piece is placed on the saw and is guided by the cut-off guide. The cross-cut guide may be clamped in position if necessary. Make the two end cuts of the gain first. Then the piece is placed on the saw with the right-hand end against the rip fence. The piece is then pushed

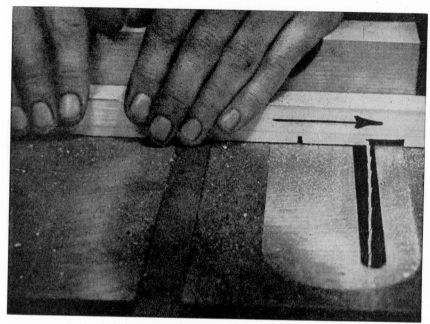

Fig. 4-16 Cutting a gain to an end cut mark.

across the saw in the direction of the arrow in the picture, until it reaches the end cut mark.

Cutting or Trimming Large Circular Pieces. Large circular pieces, such as table tops 4 or 5 feet in diameter, or pieces down to one foot in diameter, can be

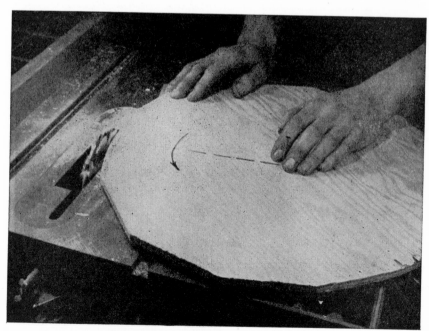

Fig. 4-17 Cutting a circular piece.

trimmed on the table saw by use of a dado head. The step-by-step procedure is as follows:

1. Raise the dado head above the table as high as possible.

2. Lay a board at least a foot wide on the table saw and, with the aid of the cross-cut guide, run it on the dado head about half-way through the board. In this position it can serve as a jig on which the work piece can rotate (Fig. 4-17).

3. After having made the layout on the work piece, run this piece on the dado head until it is tangent to the cutting edge.

4. Insert a screw or nail into the center of the piece, which will be the center of the layout circle. This will allow the piece to rotate. Then proceed to rotate the piece which will cut out the circle as the layout indicates (Fig. 4-17).

It will be noted that this is a trimming action and not an operation of sawing a circle out of a full board. The piece must be cut roughly to size so that it will push by the dado head on a circle and not bind by having projections on both sides of the cutter.

Core Box Cutting. Core box cutting on a circular saw is common practice for pattern makers. This cutting method can also be applied to concave cuts such as fluting for decorating purposes. The procedure of performing the core box cutting operation is as follows:

Set the saw at a height equal to the depth of the groove and clamp a guide at a distance from the saw equal to the measurement from the working edge of your work piece to the edge of the flute or groove.

The exact angle that the guide must be set at is found in the following manner: Two parallel lines AA' and BB' which are drawn respectively from the front and back edges of the saw where it intersects the table surface are twisted until they are at a distance equal to the desired width of the flute (Fig. 4-18). For instance, if the flute is $\frac{1}{4}''$ deep, the saw is set $\frac{1}{4}''$ above the table. If the flute is $\frac{1}{2}''$ in width, the parallel lines should show $\frac{1}{2}''$ in width when they are twisted at an angle so that they intersect the saw as described above. This is the angle at which you set the guide for the operation. At this angle, clamp the guide at a distance as described from the back edge of the saw. (See Fig. 4-19.)

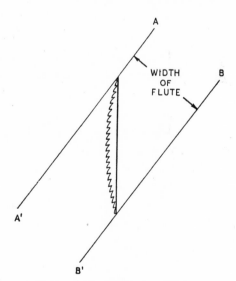

Fig. 4-18 Obtaining the angle for the guide in core box cutting.

Now you are ready to proceed to do the core box cutting (Fig. 4-19). With the guide clamped in place, and the working edge of the board against the guide, lower the saw until it projects about a $\frac{1}{16}''$ above the table, then proceed to run

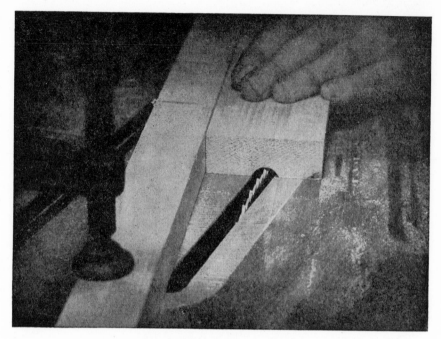

Fig. 4-19   Core box cutting.

the work piece over the saw for the first cut. After making this preliminary cut, check your setup, angle and height of saw, to see that everything is in proper adjustment. For the next cut, raise the saw until it projects about $\frac{1}{8}''$ above the table and proceed in this manner until the cut has reached the full depth. It would be well to go through this procedure first with a test piece to be sure that your setup is correct and will produce the desired effect. It will be found that you cannot take much more than a $\frac{1}{8}''$ cut with each pass because you are really pushing the work-piece more or less sideways over the saw during the cutting process.

It will also be noted that the guide is placed in such a position that when feeding the work over the saw, it wedges between the saw and guide. Some operators use two guides, one to hold either side of the piece. This is not objectionable. Another method is to use a spring-type guide on the side of the saw that is opposite the working edge. The cutting off type saw is probably the best to use in this operation as it usually has finer spaced teeth than the rip saw and is not so likely to catch into the work. A novelty saw that is in top condition, that is, properly sharpened, will make a smoother cut than a cut-off saw. The new type 8-tooth saw, which has appeared recently on the market, is also satisfactory to use for this operation, although not a very deep cut can be taken with each pass.

Cutting Moldings. Molding can be made on the circular saw by using shaped cutters similar to those which are used on a shaper, usually of the solid cutter type. At the present time, there are also on the market molder heads that use three or four individual cutters, depending upon the manufacturer's choice. You will notice that this accomplishes the operation in one pass over the cutter. The arrangement of the guide or rip fence is governed by the position that the molding cut is desired on the work piece. Many times it is advisable to rough out the molding so that the cut will not be too heavy during the finishing operation.

Another method of obtaining molding is to draw the contour of the molding on the end of the work piece and make a series of cuts with the saw raised almost up to the lay-out line on the work piece. A consecutive series of these cuts, as appears in Fig. 4-20, will give you the rough shape of the molding you desire. The rest of the shaping must be done by hand, although the sawing operation will remove the larger portion of the waste stock. In cutting molding on the circular saw, adequate arrangements must be provided for hold-downs and for holding the work piece up against the rip fence in order that a straight line feeding action can take place.

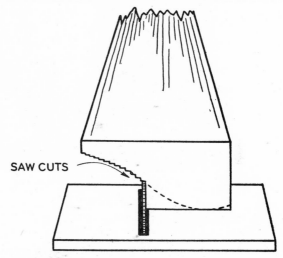

SAW CUTS

FIG. 4-20   Cutting a molding by a series of saw kerfs.

Using the Dado Head. One of the handiest accessories that are available to a person using the circular saw is the dado head. It is used mainly for making rabbets and grooves, and is in action similar to a thick circular saw blade except that it can be set up for various thicknesses, depending upon the inserts used. It will enable you to cut a dado or groove in one pass, thus saving you considerable time. Cuts can be made both with and across the grain, and small hinge gains can be made in one pass over the dado head if it is set up to the width equal to the length of the hinge. Stop-dadoes, as Fig. 4-21 shows, can be made by the same operation as performed by the wobble saw in making stop dados. The picture shows how the stops are placed when making a stop dado. They are placed exactly the same whether making a stop dado with a wobble saw or with a dado head. It shows that the setup for the stop dado is limited at both ends. *Caution:* When placing a work piece over the dado head, it should be lowered very gradually making sure there is no longitudinal slippage. That is what the stop is for on the following end of the piece. This procedure without a stop dado is a cause of many accidents. Stop-grooves can be made by the same method with the rip fence as a guide and a stop block clamped in proper position to serve as a stop when starting the stop dado.

Cutting Dovetails. True dovetails can be cut on the circular saw if there is enough work to justify making a setup. A setup includes a combination of angular

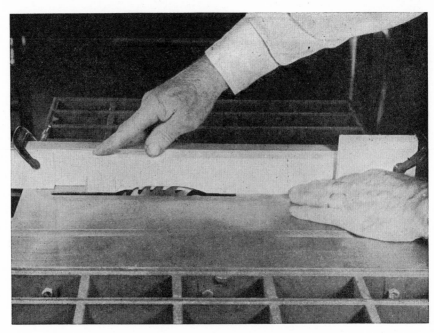

FIG. 4-21 Cutting a stop dado.

cuts by using the cut-off guide and the tilting arbor or the cut-off guide and the tilting table. Before proceeding with any cuts at all on the circular saw, it is necessary that the work be laid out completely on both the pin end and the tail end of the joint.

A procedure for cutting dovetails on the circular saw is as follows: When cutting the pin end, the saw should be set at a height above the table equal to the length of the pin. The cut-off guide should be set at an angle equal to the angle on the pin. A board is fastened to the cut-off guide long enough to protrude by the saw. Then a kerf is made in the board while in this position, and it is against this board that the work piece is held when making the cut-off as the layout indicates.

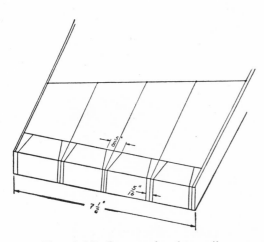

FIG. 4-22 Layout for dovetail.

There are two methods that can be used when making these cuts. First you may work directly from the layout line on all cuts. Second, if you have many pieces to cut, you can have them spaced at equal distances from each other (the cuts) and then have a stop gauge to put the pieces against when you make the corresponding cuts on the different pieces. Make all the angular cuts on one side of the pin one way first. Then reverse the cross-cut guide to the same reading on the other side of the 90° mark and make the other angular cuts, being sure that you have a board long enough to go completely by the saw which acts as a secondary guide and in which it will make a saw kerf when pushed by the saw as indicated when beginning the operation. This will give you a good support for your work piece when making the dovetail cut. After the angular cuts have been made, it is next necessary to take out the remaining wood by repeated cuts over the saw. Be sure that the saw is jointed correctly and that the periphery of the saw leaves a finished surface on the cut as it leaves the wood. This will give you a good seat for the tails as they enter and lock with the pins.

The procedure for cutting the tails is similar to that for cutting the pins except that the table is tilted, or the arbor is tilted, depending on which type table you use. The layout will give you the angle at which to tilt the table (Fig. 4-22). It is wise to make the outside cuts first and then remove the waste stock between the two cuts. You will note that in removing the waste material between the two cuts on the tails, you can only rough-cut with the saw tilted at an angle. Finishing the seat of the tail will have to be done with a hand tool. Probably it is best to work a large portion of this out by hand, although the center portion can be cut out with the saw in a vertical position, set at the correct height, which, of course, is the length of the tail. This will assure you of a flat surface when the pins enter the two tail pieces. That portion of the angle which remains must be worked out by hand.

Resawing. Resawing is a process of cutting a board of given thickness into two

Fig. 4-23   Resawing.

thinner boards. The operation is primarily a ripping one, and if the saw reaches high enough above the table so that the sawing can be done in two passes, the resawing can be accomplished completely on the saw table. This operation is of considerable importance in the home workshop, for it makes the process of getting out thin materials much quicker than surfacing a board down, with the resulting loss of time and material. The operation consists of:

1. Set the rip fence to get the correct thickness board, plus an allowance for smoothing.

2. Set the table saw at its maximum height, at least as high as the distance to the middle of the piece, if possible (Fig. 4-23). If the saw does not reach halfway through the piece, oftentimes a cut taken on each edge of the piece, as indicated in the picture, plus a pass on the band saw, makes for efficient operation.

This means that if you sawed an 8″ board up 3″ on one side and 3″ on the other side, you would leave 2″ in the middle. The 2″ remaining strip can be sawed on the band saw, thus completing the resawing job.

Cutting the Mortise-and-Tenon Joint. If the craftsman wants to make a mortise-and-tenon joint, he may make one-half of this joint with the use of the table saw. The tenon part can completely be made on the saw, while the mortise will necessarily be chiseled out with hand tools or bored out on the drill press and then finished with the use of hand tools.

The usual procedure for sawing a tenon on a table saw is as follows:

1. Secure a piece of wood of correct dimensions and, by using a cut-off guide and setting the rip fence at a distance from the saw equal to the length of the

Fig. 4-24   Cutting the shoulders of a tenon.

tenon, plus the thickness of the saw, you have your setup for making the shoulders of the tenon. Make sure that the stock to be removed comes out of the waste material. Fig. 4-24 shows the operation in process. If a piece is to be shaped on both ends, be sure that both sides of both ends are cut before changing the setting of the fence or the height of the saw.

2. After this process, the cheek cuts are made. To do this, the saw must be set at a height equal to the length of the tenon (Fig. 4-25).

3. Set the rip fence so that the waste piece is between the saw and rip fence. This insures that an equal amount will be taken off both sides. A test piece should be used in all of these settings so that, in case the cut is not correct, one of the work pieces will not be ruined.

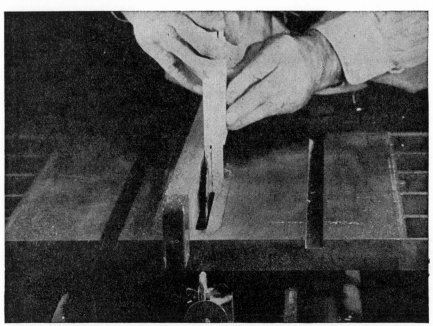

FIG. 4-25   The saw set to height for tenon (cheek cuts).

4. By placing the work piece against the rip fence, you have a bearing surface for the piece being cut. If it is cut with the waste piece on the outside, the second cut on the tenon will not have a bearing surface to help hold it vertically.

5. The fence should be set very carefully and care should be taken to hold the piece tight up against the rip fence and run completely by the saw. If it is a plain mortise and tenon, this will finish the tenon. Of course, if the tenon is not in the middle of the piece, two settings will be required for the face cuts, one for each side.

In case it is haunched mortise-and-tenon, the haunch may be cut on the saw by the same methods used in making the face cuts. Many times it is as fast to make this haunch by hand as it is to set up a saw table unless there are a lot of pieces on which similar cuts are made.

The Slip Joint. The slip joint is a special adaptation of the mortise-and-tenon joint. You will notice from the diagram (Fig. 4-26) that one end of the slip joint is exactly the same as the tenon in the mortise-and-tenon joint. The other end is made by cutting out the material that is normally saved in making the tenon. In other words, by repeated cuts and passing the work over the saw set at the right measurements, the middle of the other piece can be taken out as indicated on the drawing. This is made by holding the piece vertically against the rip fence and passing over the saw several times until all the waste material has been taken out.

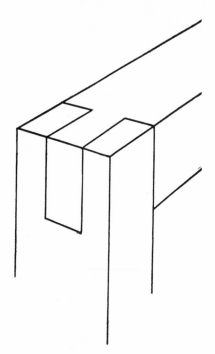

FIG. 4-26   Slip joint.

Taper Cutting on the Table Saw. Taper cuts can be made on the table saw by use of a jig, shown in Fig. 4-27 and in Project 6. You will notice that the jig is an arrangement that slides against the rip fence and, usually, the slim end of the piece being cut follows rather than leads the work. The procedure is as follows:

1. Place the jig against the rip fence.

2. Place the work piece in the proper position as indicated in Fig. 4-27. You will notice that the push block of the jig (Fig. 4-27) serves to move the work piece.

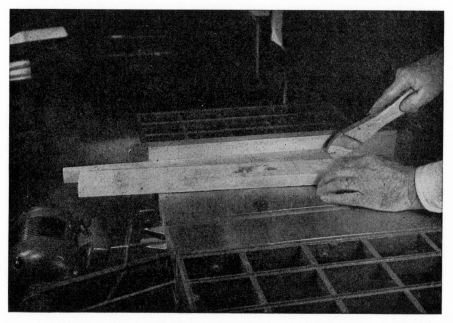

FIG. 4-27   Cutting a taper with a simple taper jig.

3. Hold the work piece against the jig with the left hand and push the jig with the right hand. A ripping cut takes place, giving the angle as laid out on the jig.

Note: Only one angle can be cut by using a solid jig. However, in Project 6 an adjustable jig is shown, by use of which vary-ing angles may be cut. It will also be noticed that this method is only practical for slim tapers and not for steep tapers. Tapered table legs are made in this manner.

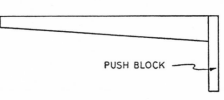

FIG. 4-28   Simple solid jig for taper sawing.

Spline Joint. A spline joint is a standard joint used in several forms of joinery. It is made similar to a tongue and groove joint and is usually used on one or two types of miter joints—either in a type joint that has a miter running across the thickness of the board, or a joint that has a miter running across the face of the board as in a picture frame.

The procedure is as follows: Select a working face of the two pieces in which the spline is to be inserted. After this has been marked, make the layout of the spline on the two pieces to determine what dimensions are advisable (Fig. 4-29).

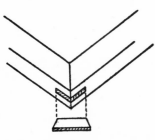

FIG. 4-29   Splined miter.

Usually the spline should not be more than $\frac{1}{3}$ the total thickness of the piece in which it is inserted. For ex-ample, if the piece is to be inserted in a joint similar to a picture frame, and if the picture frame is $\frac{3}{4}''$ thick, the spline would not be more than $\frac{1}{4}''$ thick. Many times it is less than $\frac{1}{3}$ the thickness.

The depth of the groove for the spline is usually equal to twice the thickness of the spline. After the joint has been laid out, set the rip fence and saw the grooves similar to the description of making grooves given on p. 38. Be sure that the grooves on the two pieces are located at exactly the same distance from the working face.

After the grooves have been cut, get out a sample piece for the spline. Splines should be made so that they fit snugly in the groove. Splines are usually made of hardwood and are usually made with the grain running the long way of the spline. Sometimes splines are made with the grain running across the width of the spline. This kind of spline is, of course, stronger but is more difficult to make. The reason for making the sample spline is to make sure your measure-ments in setting up the rip fence are correct.

It is essential that the spline be cut with a smooth-cutting saw and that the saw is sharp, otherwise the spline may be of varying thicknesses when it is finished. Before inserting the spline into the grooves, it is well to round off all four inside corners. The splines are inserted and glue is used as a bond to hold the pieces together. Clamping of the assembly is also essential.

V

Projects

1. Push Stick
2. Feather Board
3. Hanging Telephone Stand
4. Trellis
5. Tenoning Jig
6. Jig for Taper Sawing
7. Saw Filing Vise
8. Saw Horse
9. Serving Tray
10. Lawn Table and Two Benches
11. Stand for 8" Circular Saw
12. Coldframe
13. Circular Coffee Table
14. Bachelor's Chair with Swivel Back
15. Trapeze and Swing Set
16. Nest of Tables
17. Night Stand
18. Drawer for Night Stand
19. Cocktail Table
20. Side Tables
21. Corner Table
22. Serving Table
23. Step Table
24. Gate-Leg Drop-Leaf Table
25. Cabinet for Dinette
26. Record Cabinet
27. Tiered Bookcase
28. Machinist's Tool Chest

1. PUSH STICK

A push stick is one of the most necessary accessories needed in performing ripping operations on the table saw. Use of this device permits the operator to push stock past the saw blade without placing the pushing hand dangerously close to the blade. The owner of a table saw should make a push stick as one of his very first projects. Most of the operations in the making of this device are to be done on a jig saw or with a coping saw.

Materials Needed:

1 pc., $\frac{1}{2}'' \times 2\frac{1}{4}'' \times 12''$ maple

Procedure (see Fig. 5-1):

1. Obtain a piece of $\frac{1}{2}''$ maple and square it to the required dimensions, $2\frac{1}{4}'' \times 12''$.
2. On the face of the piece of stock, lay out the desired shape as shown in the drawing.
3. Set the cross-cut guide at a 45° angle and cut one end of the stock as shown.
4. With a jig saw or a coping saw, cut out the outline of the push stick.
5. Smooth the edges and corners with a file and sandpaper.

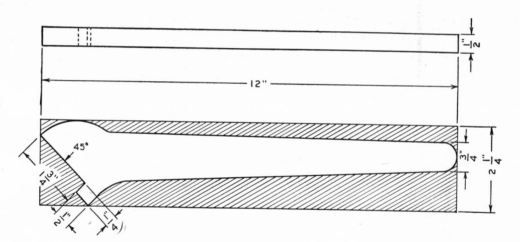

Fig. 5-1.

2. FEATHER BOARD

The feather board is a device used to steady the work on the saw table while performing various operations. It is advisable for the operator of a table saw to construct a feather board soon after purchasing the machine as this device will be used often. It can be used for steadying the stock while resawing, while cutting bevels and chamfers, and while cutting tenons.

Materials Needed:

1 pc., $\frac{7}{8}''$ × 6'' × 20'' ash

Procedure (see Fig. 5-2):

1. Square a piece of hardwood, such as ash, to the required dimensions, $\frac{7}{8}''$ × 6'' × 20''.
2. Set the cut-off guide at a 30° angle and cut off one end of the stock as shown.
3. Measure 7'' from the end just cut, and draw a line parallel to this end.
4. Set the ripping fence $\frac{1}{4}''$ from the inside of the saw blade and make a saw kerf to the guide line.
5. Continue making a series of new kerfs across the width of the stock, leaving $\frac{1}{4}''$ between each saw kerf.

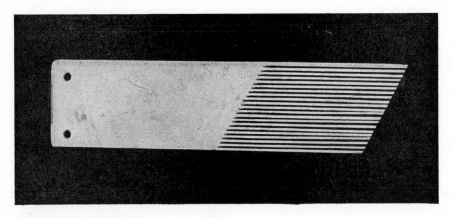

FIG. 5-2.

3. HANGING TELEPHONE STAND

This telephone stand is styled in the famous Greek motif. It has two platforms. The top platform provides space for a telephone, and the lower platform may be used as a desk for a telephone memo-address book. There is also space for small, decorative bric-a-brac.

The stand can be made from practically any kind of wood. Clear white pine is excellent. The frugal craftsman can construct the project from the wood obtained from the ends of orange crates or other scrap wood. The project can be finished to suit individual tastes and to match or high-light varying decorative schemes. Stained and shellacked or lacquered red, black, white, or chartreuse, this project is actually a handsome and practical piece of furniture.

Materials Needed:

1 pc., $\frac{3}{4}''$ × 8″ × 54″ white pine

Procedure (see Fig. 5-3):

1. Obtain a board which is $\frac{3}{4}''$ thick, over 8″ wide, and at least $4\frac{1}{2}$ feet in length. (See Fig. 5-3a.)
2. Rip the entire board to a width of 8″.
3. Square one end.
4. Cut off two pieces of wood, 10″ in length, using the stop-block and the cut-off guide.
5. Readjust the stop-block and cut off four pieces 8″ in length.
6. Select three of the 8″ pieces. Rip a piece 4″ wide from each of these (see Fig. 5-3a). Be sure to use the push stick.
7. Select two pieces of wood which remain from the first and second 8″ pieces. Rip a 3″ piece from each one (see Fig. 5-3a).
8. From the fourth 8″ piece, rip two pieces of wood 2″ in width. It will be noticed from a study of Fig. 5-3a that the grain of the wood runs lengthwise with each piece of wood that has been cut from the board.
9. Sand all pieces. Assemble project as shown in Fig. 5-3b. Use finishing nails or flathead wood screws. Finish and fasten to wall.

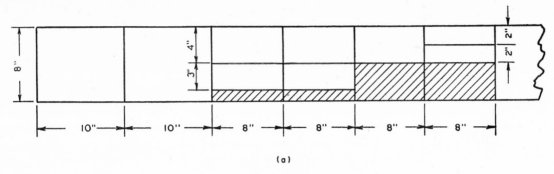

(a)

Fig. 5-3(a).

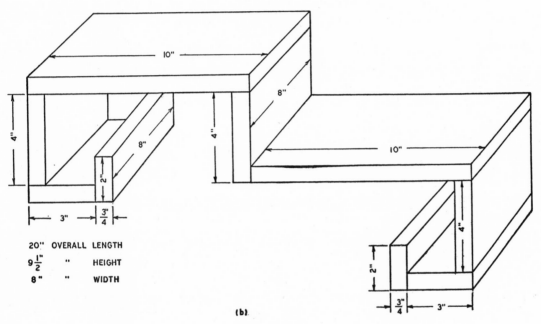

20" OVERALL LENGTH

9½" " HEIGHT

8" " WIDTH

(b)

Fig. 5-3(b).

55

4. TRELLIS

Anyone owning a yard with a few flowering bushes will have need for a trellis. This is a very simple project to make, and it adds greatly to the beauty of the yard or garden. The trellis described here is only a suggested style, and the hobbyist can develop many different styles to suit his own individual tastes. Even using the one here described, the appearance can be changed by spreading the slats to a greater amount of space.

Materials Needed:

1 pc., $1\frac{1}{4}''$ × $4''$ × $6'$ white pine (clear)
30 1'' box nails $\frac{1}{2}$ pt. outside paint

Procedure (see Fig. 5-4):

1. Rip three pieces $\frac{1}{4}''$ wide the entire length of the board. These pieces will be used as the spreaders, "A," "B," and "C" and for the trim at "D."

2. Measure 21'' from one end and square a line around the piece of stock. This line indicates where the saw cut should stop.

3. Make a pencil mark or a chalk mark on the side of the ripping fence to act as a guide so that you will end each saw cut on the line drawn on the piece of stock.

4. Set the ripping fence so that a saw cut will be made exactly in the center of the stock. Make the first cut, but be sure to stop on the line.

5. Divide the stock remaining on one side of the saw kerf into four equal parts, taking in consideration the width of the saw kerf. A cut should be taken on a piece of scrap wood in order to measure the exact width of the saw kerf.

6. Set the ripping fence so that the saw will cut in the center of the mark nearest to the center saw kerf.

7. Without changing the setting of the fence, turn the piece of stock over and make the next cut on the other side of the center kerf.

8. Continue moving the fence toward the saw so that a cut can be made on each of the space marks. Take two cuts with each setting, first on one side of the center kerf, then on the other.

9. Take one of the strips (supporting strips) that was ripped from the original piece of stock and, starting from the center, mark off equal spaces, one space for each slat. Nail the long strip to each slat as shown in the drawing ("A"). (Use 1'' box nails.)

10. Nail on strips "B" and "C" as shown and cut off to size.

11. From the remaining strip of stock, cut pieces to size for trim and nail on as shown at "D."

12. Paint the trellis as desired.

13. To erect the trellis, obtain a piece of "two-by-four" about three feet long. Sharpen one end with a hatchet and drive the stake in the ground, leaving $1\frac{1}{2}''$ above the surface. Now the trellis can be nailed to this support.

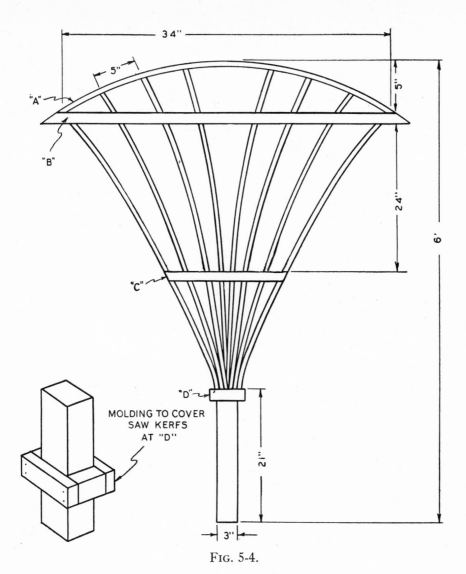

34"

5"

5"

"A"

"B"

24"

6'

"C"

"D"

MOLDING TO COVER
SAW KERFS
AT "D"

21"

3"

Fig. 5-4.

5. TENONING JIG

The tenoning jig (Fig. 5-6) is a very simple device to construct. It is extremely useful for holding the stock while cutting the cheeks of tenons. The stock may be held securely in an upright position, thus giving greater assurance of accuracy in the cutting of tenons and safer operation of the saw. Some close-grained, kiln-dried hardwood should be used, since this device will be used many times over a period of years.

Materials Needed:

1 pc., base:	$1\frac{3}{4}'' \times 4\frac{1}{2}'' \times 24''$	birch
1 pc., clamp and support:	$\frac{3}{4}'' \times 1\frac{1}{2}'' \times 20''$	birch
1 carriage bolt $\frac{1}{4}'' \times 4''$ with washer and wing nut		
1 hinge $1'' \times 1\frac{1}{2}''$		

Procedure (see Fig. 5-5):

1. Square a piece of stock to $1\frac{3}{4}'' \times 4\frac{1}{2}'' \times 24''$.
2. From the piece of $\frac{3}{4}'' \times 1\frac{1}{2}''$ stock, cut the piece for the support 8″ long. Also cut the two pieces for the clamp as shown in the drawing.
3. On one end of the support, cut a rabbet $\frac{1}{2}'' \times 2''$ as shown.
4. In the center of the hinged clamp, bore a $\frac{1}{4}''$ hole for the carriage bolt, as shown.
5. Fasten the hinge to the two pieces of the clamp.
6. Fasten the support and the hinged clamp to the base with flathead screws as shown. Be sure the support is at right angles to the base.
7. Close the hinged clamp and mark the position of the hole for the carriage bolt on the base.
8. Bore a $\frac{1}{4}''$ hole through the base and counterbore the hole on the back of the base to permit the head of the bolt to be flush with the surface of the stock.
9. Glue a piece of felt or thin rubber on the inside face of the clamp.
10. Insert the bolt, washer and wing nut as shown.

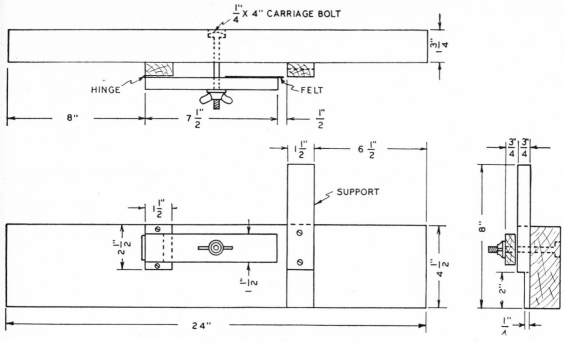

FIG. 5-5(a).

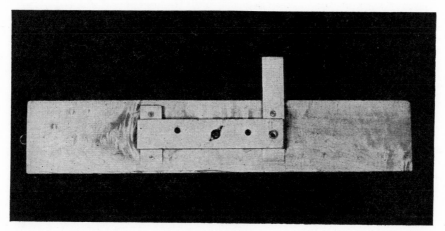

FIG. 5-5(b).

59

6. JIG FOR TAPER SAWING

This jig for taper sawings on the bench saw should be made of hardwood, preferably birch, maple, beech or some similar wood so that it can withstand rough usage. The drawing (Fig. 5-6) shows two pieces of wood which should be sawed to a dimension that will be practical for use on your bench saw. For the ordinary bench saw which has a top of about 18″—24″, pieces 24″ long will serve very nicely.

Material Needed:

2 pc., beams:	1″ × 4″ × 24″	birch
1 pc., stop block:	1″ × 4″ × 4″	birch
1 pc., clamping piece:	$\frac{1}{8}$″ × 1″ × 10″	brass

Procedure (see Fig. 5-6):

1. Lay out the above material according to the dimensions given on the drawing. The rip cuts can be made by using a temporary jig on the bench saw as described in taper sawing (p. 48) or they can be sawed out and finished by hand. Glue the stop block to the side of the adjustable beam.

2. Lay out the brass piece and drill the holes to make the slot. Make the slot as required in the clamping piece. (See "A.") Fasten the two beams together at the end with a $1\frac{3}{4}$″ hinge. Assemble the clamping piece.

3. Give one coat of shellac.

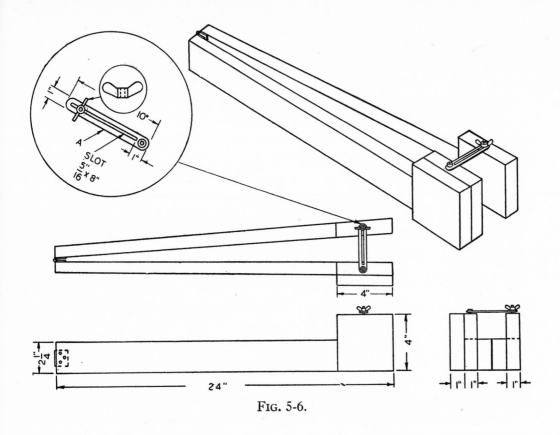

SLOT
$\frac{5}{16}" \times 8"$

FIG. 5-6.

7. SAW FILING VISE

The saw filing vise is a convenient accessory which is used to hold circular saws during the sharpening process. The one described below was designed to hold a 10″ saw. It may be clamped to the side of a bench or held in a wood or metal vise. As shown in the drawing the jaws have hexagonal contours, but this vise may also be made with circular-shaped jaws if preferred.

Materials Needed:

1 pc., support:	$\frac{3}{4}″ \times 8″ \times 14″$	Hardwood
1 pc., front jaw:	$\frac{3}{4}″ \times 8″ \times 10″$	Hardwood
1 carriage bolt:	$\frac{1}{2}″ \times 2\frac{1}{2}″$	
1 wing nut:	$\frac{1}{2}″$	
1 washer:	$\frac{1}{2}″$	
2 hinges:	$\frac{3}{4}″ \times 1\frac{1}{4}″$	
12 wood screws:	No. 6 $\times \frac{7}{8}″$ F.H.	

Procedure (see Fig. 5-9):

1. Saw out the stock to make the support and front jaw.
2. Lay out and cut the hexagonal shapes on the support and front jaw. These angular cuts may be done by utilizing the cross-cut clamp attachment.
3. Saw the chamfers on the back of the support and the front of the front jaw.
4. Locate and bore the $\frac{1}{2}″$ holes for the carriage bolt.
5. Attach the front jaw to the support by means of the two hinges.
6. Finish as desired.
7. If desired, strips of leather about $\frac{1}{16}″$ thick and $\frac{3}{4}″$ wide may be tacked to the jaws where they contact the saw.

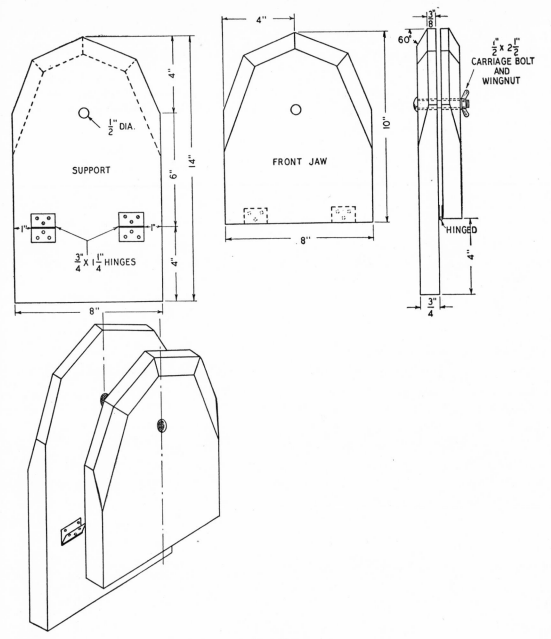

$\frac{1}{2}$" DIA.

SUPPORT

4"

14"

6"

$\frac{3}{4}$" X 1$\frac{1}{4}$" HINGES

1"

1"

4"

8"

4"

FRONT JAW

10"

8"

$\frac{3}{8}$"

60°

$\frac{1}{2}$" x 2$\frac{1}{2}$" CARRIAGE BOLT AND WINGNUT

HINGED

4"

$\frac{3}{4}$"

FIG. 5-7.

63

8. SAW HORSE

The saw horse is a very handy household accessory. It is used primarily as a support when sawing boards by hand. The ends or sides are ordinarily used for cross-cutting, and the slot between the top boards provides a convenient means of ripping. The saw horse is also used as a support for scaffolding on a variety of jobs such as painting or papering. For this reason it is usually built in pairs. It may be built of most any type of wood, but must be of sturdy construction to stand up under its normal usage.

Materials Needed:

2 pc., side boards:	$\frac{13}{16}'' \times 7'' \times 30''$	pine
2 pc., end boards:	$\frac{13}{16}'' \times 7'' \times 12\frac{1}{2}''$ (min.)	pine
2 pc., top boards:	$\frac{13}{16}'' \times 6'' \times 31\frac{1}{2}''$	pine
4 pc., legs:	$1\frac{5}{8}'' \times 3\frac{5}{8}'' \times 18''$	spruce or hemlock

Procedure (see Fig. 5-8):

1. From $\frac{13}{16}''$ thick boards, rip enough material 7'' wide to obtain the two side boards and two end boards. The length for the end boards given in the table is a minimum dimension, and the angles on these boards will be cut later.
2. Rip enough material 6'' wide to make the two top boards.
3. Square the side and top boards to length.
4. Square the legs to length.
5. Set a T-bevel to an angle of 5°.
6. Obtain two pieces of 7'' wide material at least 13'' long and lay out the guide lines for the angular cuts on them. Refer to drawing for dimensions.
7. Set the cross-cut guide to make these angular cuts (approximately 5°).
8. Saw off one end of each piece.
9. Carefully saw off the other ends. It is important that the two end pieces be of the same length and shape.
10. Nail or screw the end pieces to the legs. It is good practice to nail one set of legs to an end board and then check the second set to the first before the final nailing.
11. Nail or screw the side boards to the legs.
12. Nail or screw the top boards in place.
13. Finish as desired.

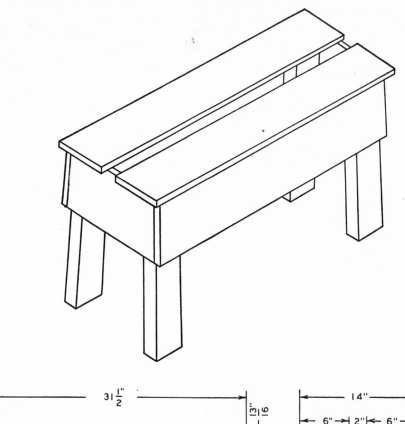

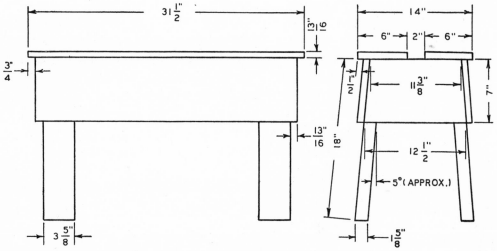

FIG. 5-8.

65

9. SERVING TRAY

This serving tray could be made of tropical woods and finished naturally with some of the new plastic varnishes so that it would be resistant to heat and alcohol. It is made entirely of wood and put together with one of the plastic glues and either brass or chrome roundhead screws, or else nailed, with holes filled with an appropriate filler after assembly. It is a size designed to be especially useful with a coffee table. The mitered corners can be held together by small clamp nails or brads. Other methods may be used such as dovetailing the corners.

The material used in the bottom of this tray is specifically mahogany veneer because it does not swell, shrink, or warp as readily as solid wood of the same dimension. The rest of the tray is made from solid mahogany. The size given in the list of materials is block size needed from which to fabricate the handles. Make all cuts on the saw table with a novelty saw blade.

Materials Needed:

1 pc., bottom:	$\frac{5}{16}'' \times 11\frac{7}{16}'' \times 19\frac{7}{16}''$	mahogany veneer
2 pc., sides:	$\frac{5}{16}'' \times 1\frac{5}{16}'' \times 20''$	mahogany
2 pc., ends:	$\frac{5}{16}'' \times 1\frac{5}{16}'' \times 12''$	mahogany
1 pc., handles:	$\frac{7}{8}'' \times 1\frac{5}{8}'' \times 8\frac{1}{2}''$	mahogany

Glue; nails; screws; putty; brads; finishing material

Procedure (see Fig. 5-9):

1. By the use of the rip fence and cross-cut guide, cut the bottom piece to the correct size.

2. Saw the side and end pieces to the correct cross section.

3. All joints should be layed out as per sample on the drawing. Make a rabbet in the bottom edge of both the sides and the ends as per basic operations. Sand all pieces carefully and assemble the tray thus far.

4. Make the miter cut on the ends and sides by use of the cross-cut guide.

5. The handles can be made in one piece. Then saw the piece in two parts after it is shaped.

6. Make a rabbeted effect on the outside of the handle as indicated on the detailed drawing. The top of the handle is best shaped by hand, and the inside curve on the bottom can be shaped by use of the band saw after the handles have been cut in two, or it can be worked out by hand with the aid of a gouge. Assemble handles with the glue and screws.

7. Look the tray over carefully and prepare it for finishing.

8. Stain or finish natural.

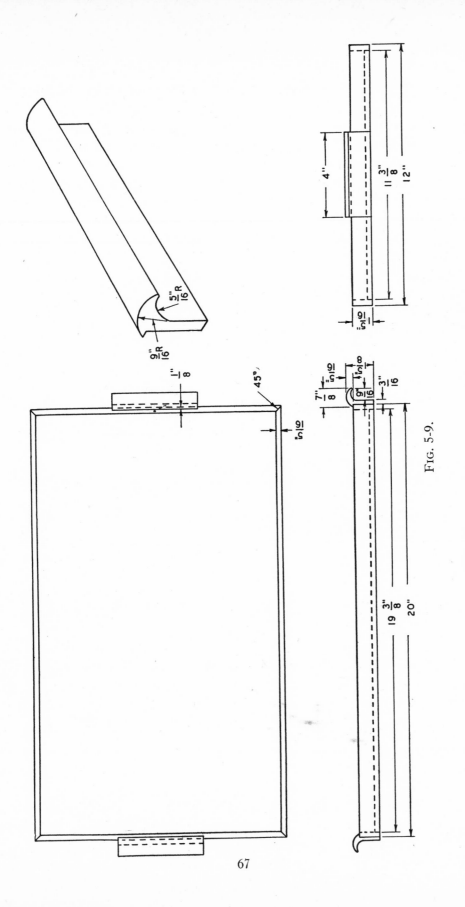

$\frac{5"}{16}$ R

$\frac{9"}{16}$ R

$\frac{1"}{8}$

45°

$\frac{5}{16}$

4"

$11\frac{3}{8}$

12"

$1\frac{5}{16}$"

$\frac{5}{16}$

$\frac{5}{16}$

$\frac{8}{16}$

$\frac{9}{16}$

$\frac{7"}{16}$

$\frac{3"}{16}$

$19\frac{3}{8}$

20"

Fig. 5-9.

10. LAWN TABLE AND TWO BENCHES

This set of outdoor furniture is planned both from a practical and from a weather resistant point-of-view. It can be made of white pine, although there are many other woods that can be used, such as fir, hemlock, cypress, cedar, redwood, or chestnut, all of which are quite resistant to the weather. Most of them present a good appearance when finished in the natural.

Practically all of the cutting can be done on the bench saw as it involves resawing, ripping, and cross-cutting. There are also several miter cuts that can be made with the aid of the cross-cut guide. Choice of the finish should rest with the individual making the project, although bright colors are noticeably pleasant to see in all types of outdoor furniture.

Materials Needed:

12 pc., tops for benches and table:	$1\frac{1}{2}'' \times 3\frac{1}{2}'' \times 48''$	pine
4 pc., table legs:	$1\frac{1}{2}'' \times 3\frac{1}{2}'' \times 36''$, approx.	pine
2 pc., top cross pieces for table:	$1\frac{1}{2}'' \times 3\frac{1}{2}'' \times 22''$	pine
2 pc., braces for table:	$1\frac{1}{2}'' \times 3\frac{1}{2}'' \times 24''$, approx.	pine
8 pc., bench legs:	$1\frac{1}{2}'' \times 3\frac{1}{2}'' \times 18''$, approx.	pine
4 pc., bench braces:	$1\frac{1}{2}'' \times 3\frac{1}{2}'' \times 20''$	pine
4 pc., bench cross pieces:	$1\frac{1}{2}'' \times 3\frac{1}{2}'' \times 10''$	pine

Bolts, screws, and finishing material

(Materials being used should be surfaced to $1\frac{1}{2}''$ thick, or if the ordinary run of 2×4's are used, they can be resawed to this thickness according to the instructions given in Basic Operations.)

Procedure for the Table (see (a) of Fig. 5-10):

1. Rip 12 top pieces of the material $3\frac{1}{2}''$ wide and square off the ends so that each is 4 feet in length.

2. Set the T-bevel from the angle given on the drawing and lay out the ends of the legs. After laying out the legs, set the cross-cut guide to the layout angle and saw off the ends of the legs for the table.

3. Square off the two top cross pieces of the same cross section, 22" long.

4. Procedure for notching the two top cross pieces: Make a layout on the top cross pieces as indicated on the drawing. You will note that there is a long rip cut to be made and a short cross-cut on each of these cross pieces. This long rip cut can be made on the saw table by using the stop-cut procedure, described in the basic operations. The cross-cut, which is short, can be made with a hand saw.

5. Now make the layout for the holes on the legs by locating the center bolt hole in each of the legs and bore with a $\frac{3}{8}''$ bit.

6. Locate the two holes in the end of each leg and bore a hole with a $\frac{1}{4}''$ bit.

7. Put the $\frac{3}{8}''$ bolts through two of the legs and spread the top of the legs so that the extreme corners are 22" apart.

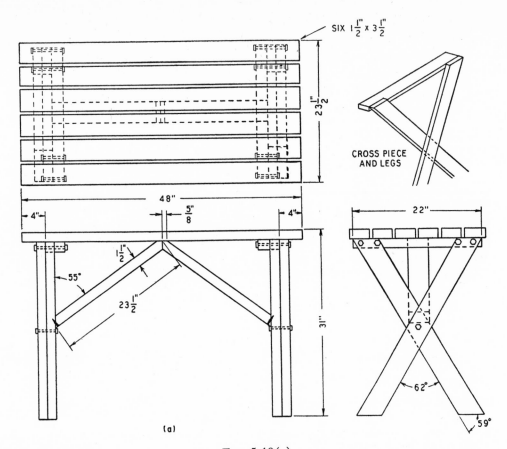

FIG. 5-10(a).

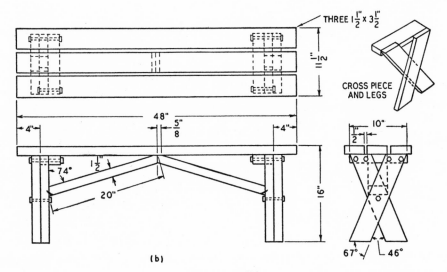

FIG. 5-10(b).

69

8. Lay these on the notched top piece and locate the holes for the bolts by which they are fastened to the top cross piece.

9. Bore the holes to receive the leg bolts in the top cross piece.

10. Sand all pieces carefully.

11. Fasten the table top pieces to the two top cross pieces, using $1\frac{3}{4}''$ No. 10 flathead brass screws.

12. Fasten the legs to the cross piece.

13. After the legs are fastened to the cross piece, turn the table, bottom side up, and check the correct length for the brace pieces, by placing the pieces in actual position on the table.

14. After the actual length is marked out, set the bevel at the correct angle and make the layout.

15. Set the saw guide to the correct angle and cut off the ends of the braces.

16. Fasten these in the correct position with screws. Test legs with table top for squaring.

17. Check all details and sand for final finish.

18. Finish as desired.

19. Procedure for making the benches is identical with that of the table. (See (b) of Fig. 5-10.)

11. STAND FOR 8'' CIRCULAR SAW

If your circular saw is not equipped with a floor stand, one of your first projects should be a sturdy wooden stand on which you can mount the saw and motor. The size of such a stand depends somewhat on the make of saw and the position of the motor mount. The stand described here will accommodate most 8'' saws of popular manufacture. A shelf may be built near the bottom for saws that require the motor to be mounted underneath the saw. A plywood top is most satisfactory, although, if it is not obtainable, the top may be planked with two or more boards.

Materials Needed:

1 pc., top:	$\frac{1}{2}'' \times 13'' \times 27''$	5-ply fir
4 pc., legs:	$1\frac{5}{8}'' \times 3\frac{5}{8}'' \times 29''$	fir
4 pc., side rails:	$\frac{13}{16}'' \times 4'' \times 25''$	white pine
2 pc., end rails (top):	$\frac{13}{16}'' \times 4'' \times (10''$ approx.)	white pine
2 pc., end rails (bot.):	$\frac{13}{16}'' \times 4'' \times (11''$ approx.)	white pine

Procedure (see Fig. 5-11):

1. From a board $\frac{13}{16}''$ thick and of sufficient width, rip material enough for the side and end rails. This may be obtained from one long board or may be cut from short stock, depending upon the available material.

2. If the rails are to be made from long material, cut each piece from the long board with a hand saw, allowing about one-half inch on each piece so that the ends may be trimmed on the machine.

3. Square off one end on each of the side rails, using the cross-cut guide.

4. Set the stop-rod gauge on the cross-cut guide and cut each of the side rails to length.

5. With a T-bevel, lay out the 5° angle cuts on each of the end rails.

6. Set the cut-off guide at 5° and saw off one end of each of the end rails.

7. Reverse the board and saw the second end on each rail.

8. The legs should be cut from standard 2'' × 4'' stock. Cut the stock with a hand saw about one-half inch longer than required.

9. Tilt the saw or table, depending upon the style of machine, at 5° and saw one end of each leg.

10. Set the stop-rod gauge for the length, and saw each leg to length.

11. Cut out the material for the top of the stand.

12. Assemble the end rails to the legs with wood screws. A stronger joint may be obtained by applying glue before fastening with wood screws.

13. Assemble the side rails and fasten the plywood top with screws.

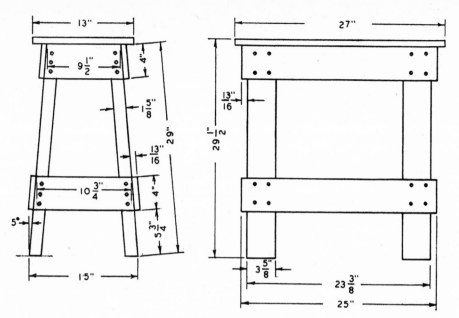

F<small>IG</small>. 5-11.

12. COLDFRAME

The coldframe can be used for seedlings in the spring, or, in the summer months, for plants which require special care. Also many garden vegetables can be grown in the fall by using the coldframe.

Materials Needed:

1 pc., back board:	$\frac{3}{4}'' \times 15'' \times 72''$	cypress or redwood
1 pc., front board:	$\frac{3}{4}'' \times 9'' \times 72''$	cypress or redwood
2 pc., side board:	$\frac{3}{4}'' \times 15'' \times 36''$	cypress or redwood
2 pc., corner braces:	$1\frac{1}{2}'' \times 1\frac{1}{2}'' \times 15''$	cypress or redwood
2 pc., corner braces:	$1\frac{1}{2}'' \times 1\frac{1}{2}'' \times 9''$	cypress or redwood
1 pc., hinge board:	$1\frac{3}{8}'' \times 2'' \times 72''$	cypress or redwood
2 or 4 hinges:	$2\frac{1}{2}'' \times 2\frac{1}{2}''$	brass
Flathead woodscrews:	No. 10—$2\frac{1}{2}''$ F.H.	brass

Procedure (see Fig. 5-12):

1. Saw out the $\frac{3}{4}''$ stock for the front, back and side boards. Use convenient widths to make up the required dimension.

2. Lay out the tapers on the side boards, and saw these tapers with the aid of the jig for tapering.

3. Saw out the $1\frac{1}{2}'' \times 1\frac{1}{2}''$ stock for the corner braces.

4. Saw the $1\frac{3}{8}''$ stock for hinge board.

5. Lay out, bore and countersink the necessary screw holes for the screws used in fastening the boards to the corner blocks. These holes should be staggered to prevent splitting.

6. For additional strength it is sometimes advisable to nail or screw cleats on the inside surface of the boards. This will prevent the joints from separating.

7. Assemble with No. 10—$2\frac{1}{2}''$ F.H. brass screws. Be sure to check for squareness while assembling.

8. Finish with good outside paint.

9. The sash for this frame may be bought either in one large sash 3 feet wide and 6 feet long or in two sections each 3 feet square. In case the 3-foot square sections are used, it is good practice to add two additional $1\frac{1}{2}'' \times 1\frac{1}{2}''$ blocks as supports under the middle of the sash frame as shown in drawing. If desired, the frame may be divided into two sections as shown in the drawing.

10. Fasten the sash in place to the hinge board with sturdy hinges. It is good practice to provide side hooks or otherwise protect the sash from damage in case they are opened and fall backwards.

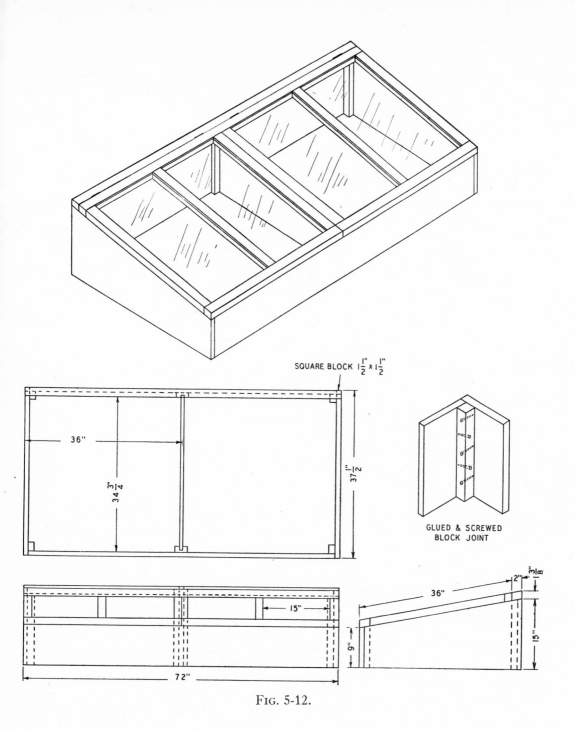

SQUARE BLOCK $1\frac{1}{2}" \times 1\frac{1}{2}"$

36"

$34\frac{3}{4}"$

$37\frac{1}{2}"$

GLUED & SCREWED
BLOCK JOINT

15"

9"

72"

36"

2"

$\frac{3}{8}"$

15"

FIG. 5-12.

75

13. CIRCULAR COFFEE TABLE

This coffee table is ideal for use with half sofas or to complete the balance for corner arrangements of furniture. The top may be cut from veneer, plywood, or glued-up stock. If the craftsman can obtain a circular piece of heavy plate glass for the top he can change the dimensions of the framework to fit.

Materials Needed:

2 cross pieces: $2'' \times 2'' \times 38''$ cabinet hardwood
4 upright pieces: $2'' \times 2'' \times 18''$ cabinet hardwood
1 piece for top: $\frac{3}{4}'' \times 38'' \times 38''$ veneer, plywood, or glued-up stock. The diameter of the *finished* circular top is 36″

Procedure (see Fig. 5-13):

1. Saw all cross pieces and upright pieces to size.
2. Lay out a cross-lap joint in the middle of each 38″ piece.
3. Cut the joint on the saw. (See use of dado in basic operations.)
4. Lay out mortises on the ends of the 38″ pieces and tenons on one end of each $18\frac{1}{2}''$ piece. Cut tenons on saw and cut mortises by hand (see Fig. A).
5. Cut circular top on saw. (See Basic Operations.)
6. Assemble framework, checking for squareness.
7. Lay top on uprights and scribe its position (see Fig. B). Make sure that the same amount of stock shows on the ends of each leg.
8. Remove the legs and lay out the rabbet on the top ends of the uprights. The rabbet should be $\frac{1}{2}'' \times \frac{3}{4}''$ (see Fig. C). Cut the rabbets on the saw.
9. Cut out the remaining curved portion with chisel and gouge (see Fig. B).
10. Sand all pieces. Assemble by gluing and clamping. Finish as desired.

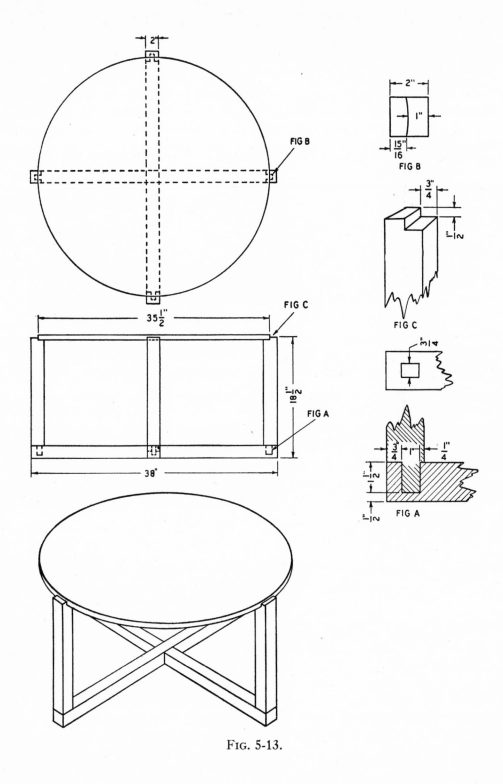

2"

FIG B

FIG C

35½"

18½"

FIG A

38"

2"

1"

15"
16

FIG B

3"
4

1"
2

FIG C

3"1⁄4

3"
4   1"
4

1"
2

1"
2

FIG A

FIG. 5-13.

14. BACHELOR'S CHAIR WITH SWIVEL BACK

This chair (Fig. 5-14) is ideal for the master bedroom or for the playroom, den, or yacht deck chair. It may be constructed from practically any kind of wood. A sturdy hardwood such as oak is preferable. The seat and back rest are made by weaving strips of heavy cowhide over the wooden framework. Old leather belting or plastic strips may be used if the craftsman has some available. The wood may be finished to suit individual tastes.

Materials Needed:

2 pc., front legs:	$2'' \times 2'' \times 30''$	white oak
2 pc., back legs:	$2'' \times 2'' \times 28''$	white oak
4 pc., side rails:	$2'' \times 2'' \times 23''$	white oak
1 pc., front seat rail:	$2'' \times 2'' \times 25''$	white oak
1 pc., back seat rail:	$2'' \times 2'' \times 25''$	white oak
2 pc., sides for the back rest:	$2'' \times 2'' \times 14\frac{1}{2}''$	white oak
1 pc., top for the back rest:	$2'' \times 2'' \times 21''$	white oak
1 pc., bottom for the back rest:	$2'' \times 2'' \times 21''$	white oak
1 steel rod:	$\frac{3}{8}'' \times 26''$	

$50\frac{1}{4}$ feet of $2''$ heavy cowhide leather stripping
  362'' for seat
  177'' for swivel back rest
  64'' for chair arms
8 dowels: $\frac{3}{8}'' \times 2''$.

Procedure (see Fig. 5-14):

1. From $2'' \times 2''$ *S4S* (Surfaced *4 S*ides) stock, saw all pieces to length. Make sure that all ends are square.

2. Lay out mortise-and-tenon joints for the four side rails and the front and back seat rails (see location of rails in Figs. B and C and joint dimensions in Fig. D).

3. Cut all tenons on saw. (See Basic Operations.) The ends of the tenons on the bottom side rails and the front and back seat rails are cut at a 45° angle as they will meet in the middle of each of the four legs (see Fig. D). This may be done by tilting the saw and trimming the ends of the tenons. The tenons may also be beveled by hand with a jack plane.

4. Cut all mortises in the legs, using the brace and bit and a chisel.

5. Round off the tops of all four legs as indicated in Figs. A and C. This may be accomplished by using a band saw or a power sander.

6. Assemble the two sides of the chair. Use glue and bar clamps.

7. Glue and clamp front and back seat rails into place.

8. Lay out slip joints on the ends of all back rest pieces (see Fig. E).

9. Cut slip joints on saw. The tenons, on the top and bottom pieces, are cut in a fashion similar to the tenons cut previously. The open mortise may be cut by taking a series of successive passes over the saw. (See Basic Operations.)

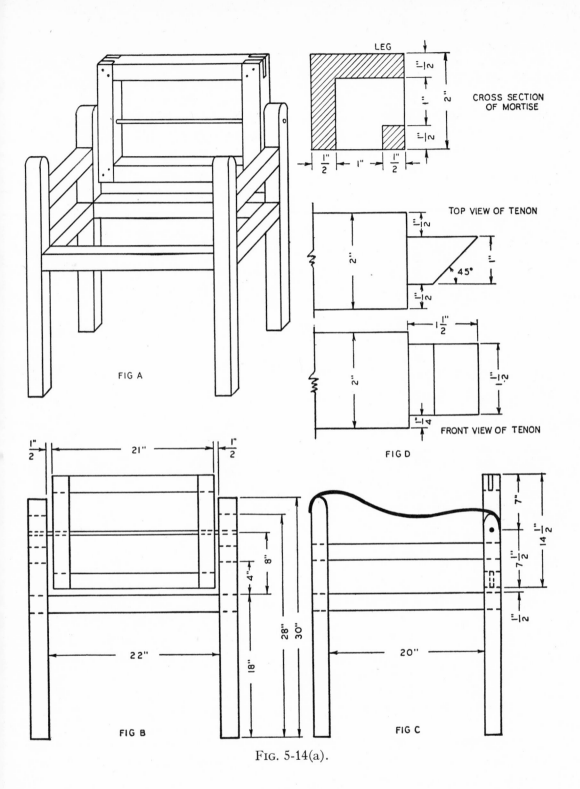

LEG

CROSS SECTION
OF MORTISE

$\frac{1}{2}$"

1"

2"

$\frac{1}{2}$"

$\frac{1}{2}$" 1" $\frac{1}{2}$"

TOP VIEW OF TENON

$\frac{1}{2}$"

2"

1"

45°

$\frac{1}{2}$"

$1\frac{1}{2}$"

2"

$\frac{1}{2}$"

$\frac{1}{4}$"

FRONT VIEW OF TENON

FIG D

FIG A

$\frac{1}{2}$"   21" $\frac{1}{2}$"

8"

4"

28"   30"

18"

22"

7"

14$\frac{1}{2}$"

7$\frac{1}{2}$"

$\frac{1}{2}$"

20"

FIG B

FIG C

FIG. 5-14(a).

79

10. Assemble the back rest, using bar clamps. Bore two $\frac{3}{8}''$ holes through the sides of each slip joint (see Fig. E). Fasten each joint by driving a $\frac{3}{8}'' \times 2''$ birch dowel, which has been dipped in glue, through each hole.

11. Lay out and bore a $\frac{3}{8}''$ hole through both sides of the back rest. The center of the hole should be $7\frac{1}{2}''$ from the bottom of the back rest (see Fig. C).

12. Lay out and bore a $\frac{3}{8}''$ hole through the sides of both back legs. The holes should be $2''$ from the tops of the legs.

13. Finish the chair to individual taste.

14. Weave $2''$ heavy leather strips over the seat frame and the back rest frame as indicated in Figs. F and G. Fasten the ends of the strips underneath each frame with large upholsterer's tacks or small flathead nails. A $\frac{3}{8}''$ hole should be punched or cut into both ends of the center cross-wise leather strip in the back rest to accommodate the steel rod (see Fig. G).

15. Using the same $2''$ leather stripping, form the arms of the chair as indicated in Fig. C. Large, decorative-headed tacks are recommended.

16. Mount the back rest into place by inserting the $\frac{3}{8}'' \times 26''$ steel rod through the back legs and the sides of the back rest.

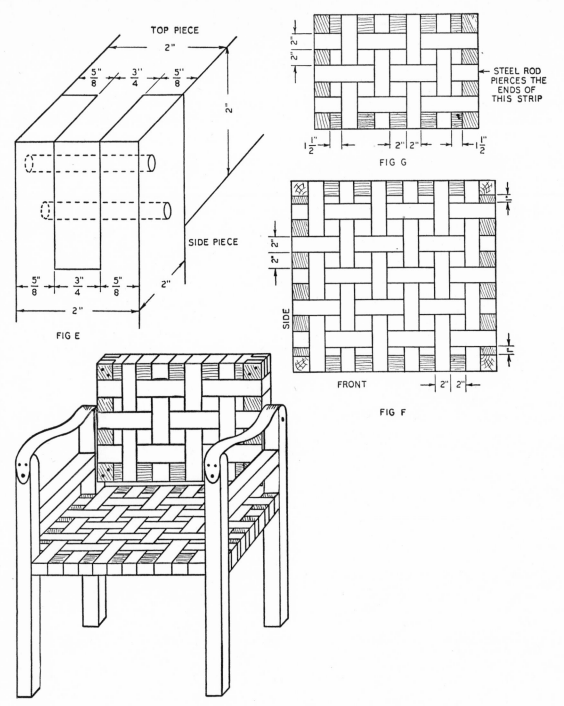

TOP PIECE

2"

$\frac{5}{8}"$ $\frac{3}{4}"$ $\frac{5}{8}"$

2"

2"

SIDE PIECE

$\frac{5}{8}"$ $\frac{3}{4}"$ $\frac{5}{8}"$

2"

2"

FIG E

2" 2"

2"

STEEL ROD
PIERCES THE
ENDS OF
THIS STRIP

$1\frac{1}{2}"$ 2" 2" $1\frac{1}{2}"$

FIG G

2" 2"

SIDE

FRONT 2" 2"

FIG F

Fig. 5-14(b).

81

15. TRAPEZE AND SWING SET

Every child gets a good deal of pleasure from an outdoor swing. Many homes, however, are located in areas where there are no trees from which a rope-swing may be suspended. The swing herein described is sturdily constructed and braced, yet it can easily be taken apart for storage during the winter months. Plans for this swing may be altered to suit individual requirements. Shortening the top rail to 6 feet and suspending a single swing will decrease the area the swing will occupy.

Materials Needed:

2 pc., base:	$2'' \times 4'' \times 12'$	fir
4 pc., legs:	$2'' \times 4'' \times 8'$	fir
3 pc., top cross bar:	$2'' \times 4'' \times 10'$	fir
2 pc., top brace:	$2'' \times 4'' \times 18''$	fir
4 pc., top plate:	$\frac{3}{4}'' \times 10'' \times 22''$	pine
2 pc., swing seat:	$\frac{3}{4}'' \times 10'' \times 20''$	pine
1 pc., trapeze rod:	$1\frac{1}{4}''D \times 20''$	ash
8 carriage bolts:	$\frac{1}{4}'' \times 7''$	
6 eye bolts:	$\frac{5}{16}'' \times 4''$	
12 flathead screws:	$2\frac{1}{2}$ #12	steel
32 flathead screws:	$1\frac{3}{4}$ #10	steel

4 steel rods, threaded on both ends: $\frac{5}{16} \times 12''$

Procedure (see Fig. 5-15):

Cross bar

1. Select the three 10-foot 2 × 4's for the top cross bar.
2. Lay out the centers for the six eye bolts and bore $\frac{5}{16}''$ holes through the center member of this cross bar.
3. Spike these 2 × 4's together, using 16 d nails. Space the nails about 10'' on centers. Drive the nails from each side of the cross bar.
4. Lay out and saw off the 45° angle on each end of this bar.

Side frame

1. Cut the 60° angle on each end of the two bases as indicated.
2. Cut the ends of the four legs at 28° and 62° as indicated.
3. Place each set of legs and the foot on a flat surface in the assembled position. Use three scrap blocks of 2 × 4 stock to gauge the space which will be occupied by the top cross bar.
4. Lay the stock to be used for the plate in position on the frame and mark the angle.
5. Saw the two top plates to the layout line.

Assembly

1. Set the cross bar in place at the top of each side frame. Temporary brace strips of shingle lath may be used, to hold the entire frame together while boring the $\frac{5}{16}''$ holes for the steel tie rods.

2. Insert the steel tie rods and bolt securely by using flat washers under the nuts.

3. Measure for the top brace piece and cut stock for each brace.

4. Fasten this top brace into place.

5. Place the stock for the inside top plate into position and lay out the angles on the end.

6. Fasten these plates into position.

Swings

1. Cut out stock for each swing seat.

2. Bore the $\frac{3}{4}''$ hole for the rope.

3. Place the six eye bolts in place.

4. Thread the $\frac{5}{8}''$ rope through the eye bolts and seat and tie securely to each eye bolt.

5. An old tool handle would be excellent material for the trapeze bar.

6. Sandpaper all surfaces and paint with three coats of paint.

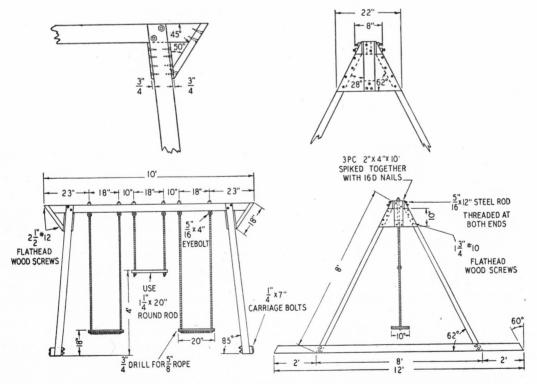

FIG. 5-15.

83

16. NEST OF TABLES

These four tables called a nest are identical in construction and can be used in the home where it is convenient to have identical tables for various uses. The ease of storage facilities is one important reason for making these tables, and the sturdy construction and the adaptability of the construction to the saw table make an interesting project. The wood used can be almost any type of cabinet wood such as birch, gum, mahogany, cherry, maple, or some of the softer woods such as pine, basswood, white wood, or poplar.

If a natural finish is desired, the techniques of finishing should be studied from some reputable manual, or the tables can be painted.

Materials Needed (4 tables):

4 pc., top:	$1'' \times 10'' \times 20''$	gum
16 pc., legs:	$1'' \times 1\frac{1}{2}'' \times 22\frac{1}{2}''$	gum
8 pc., top cross pieces:	$1'' \times 2'' \times 10''$	gum

Procedure (see Fig. 5-16):

Tops: Saw out four pieces 1″ thick × 10″ wide × 20″ long. Surface these pieces and sand for smoothness.

Top cross pieces: By the use of the cross-cut guide, saw out the eight top cross pieces of the dimensions as indicated on the drawing. Notice that the angular cuts can be made by use of the jig for tapering.

Legs: The legs are merely pieces sawed to the correct dimension by use of the rip fence. The angle on the bottom end of the leg is sawed by use of the jig for tapering.

After these pieces have been cut to size and sanded properly, the assembling of the project is as follows:

1. Fasten the two cross pieces to the top from the underneath side with $1\frac{1}{2}''$ flathead screws. These should be countersunk so that the heads will not show.

2. Glue and clamp each set of legs.

3. Note that the wedge-shaped block, which remains after sawing the angle on the top of the leg, may be used as a clamp block in this assembly.

4. After the glue is properly set, and the pieces sanded, fasten the leg assembly to the top cross piece, using glue and $1\frac{1}{4}''$ No. 8 flathead screws. Screws should be inserted from the inside. In fastening the legs to the top cross piece, be sure the center line of the leg assembly is lined up with the center line of the table top.

5. Sand thoroughly and finish as desired.

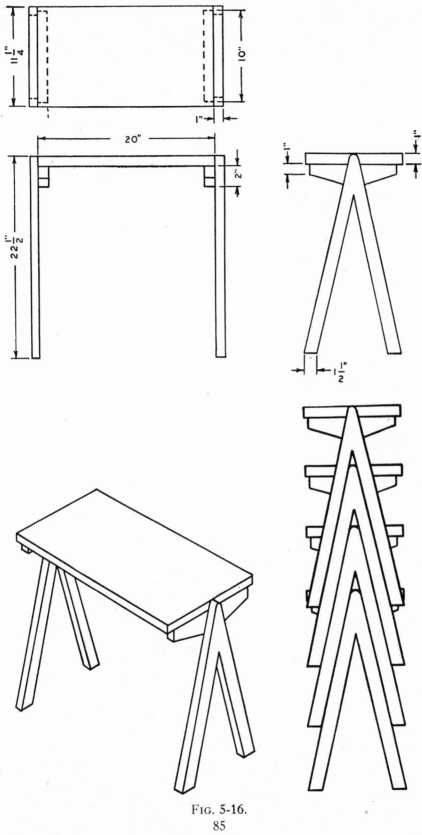

FIG. 5-16.

17. NIGHT STAND

The modern night stand described here can be made from a wood which may be finished to match an existing bedroom set. Although this project can be constructed from glued-up stock, veneer-surfaced plywood is recommended for the construction of the main panels. The drawer fronts, drawer pulls, and feet should be made of solid wood to match the grain of the plywood in the main panels. The construction of the drawers is discussed in the next project.

Materials Needed:

2 pc., top and bottom:	$\frac{3}{4}'' \times 16'' \times 18''$	veneer-surfaced plywood
2 pc., sides:	$\frac{3}{4}'' \times 18'' \times 23''$	veneer-surfaced plywood
2 pc., shelves:	$\frac{3}{4}'' \times 15\frac{1}{4}'' \times 17\frac{5}{8}''$	veneer-surfaced plywood
4 pc., feet:	$3'' \times 3'' \times 3''$	hardwood
1 pc., back panel:	$\frac{3}{8}'' \times 15\frac{1}{4}'' \times 22\frac{1}{4}''$	plywood

Procedure (see Fig. 5-17):

1. Rip a piece 18'' wide from a 7-foot panel of the selected plywood. This panel will be sufficient for the bottom, top, and sides. Of course, the equivalent may be used if this length is not obtainable.
2. Cut a $\frac{3}{8}'' \times \frac{3}{8}''$ rabbet in the edge of the 18'' piece to receive the back panel.
3. Cut the sides, top, and bottom about one inch longer than the dimensions on the drawing.
4. Set the saw for cutting the mitered ends and make one miter cut on each of the pieces.
5. Measure the exact length from the long side of the miter and make the second miter cut on each piece.
6. The mitered joint may now be grooved to receive a wooden spline. This splined joint is optional.
7. Lay out and cut the $\frac{3}{4}''$ dados in each side.
8. Rip a second piece from the plywood panel, $17\frac{5}{8}''$ wide and about 32'' long.
9. From this piece, cut two pieces, $15\frac{1}{4}''$ long, for the shelves.
10. Obtain a piece of hardwood, $3'' \times 3'' \times 13''$, for the feet.
11. Set the saw for ripping a bevel of 12° and rip this bevel on two opposite edges of the $3'' \times 3''$ piece.
12. With the saw set at the same angle, using the cut-off guide, cut off the beveled blocks as shown in the drawing. The tapered piece of waste stock from step 11 is used here to support the tapered piece against the cut-off guide.
13. Sand the surfaces of all the pieces carefully.
14. Fasten the feet to the bottom panel with $1\frac{1}{2}$ No. 10 flathead wood screws.
15. Assemble the top, bottom, and sides with glue and clamps. If a splined miter joint is not to be used, nail the miter joint from the sides with 6d finishing nails and set the heads below the surface.

16. From a piece of $\frac{3}{8}''$ plywood, cut the back panel and fasten this in place with finishing nails and glue.

17. Fill all cracks and nail holes with a suitable filler and apply the desired finish.

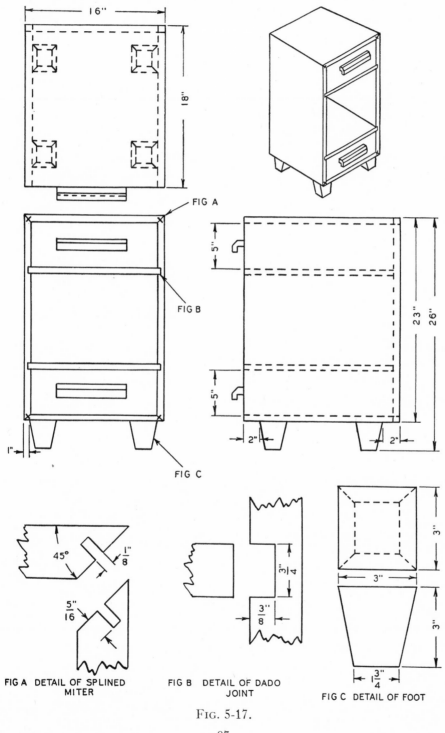

FIG A

FIG B

FIG C

FIG A DETAIL OF SPLINED MITER

FIG B DETAIL OF DADO JOINT

FIG C DETAIL OF FOOT

FIG. 5-17.

18. DRAWER FOR NIGHT STAND

There are many occasions when a piece of cabinet work requires a drawer. The drawer described here in detail is designed to fit the night stand which was described in the previous project. Since most drawer construction is basically the same as herein described, this project may be altered to suit the purpose for which it is to be used by merely changing the dimensions.

Materials Needed for One Drawer:

1 pc., front:	$\frac{3}{4}'' \times 5'' \times 14\frac{1}{2}''$	hardwood to match stand
2 pc., sides:	$\frac{1}{2}'' \times 5'' \times 16''$	birch
1 pc., back:	$\frac{1}{2}'' \times 4\frac{1}{4}'' \times 14''$	birch
1 pc., bottom:	$\frac{1}{4}'' \times 14'' \times 15\frac{3}{4}''$	plywood
1 pc., 2 handles:	$1\frac{1}{2}'' \times 1\frac{1}{2}'' \times 16''$	hardwood to match stand

If two or more drawers are to be made the same size, make them all at once rather than one at a time.

Procedure (see Fig. 5-18):

1. Get out the stock for the front and two sides.
2. Cut a $\frac{1}{4}''$ groove in the front and two sides to receive the drawer bottom.
3. Cut the back piece equal in width to the distance from the top of the drawer to the groove.
4. Lay out and cut the dovetail joints. (If desired, a rabbet joint may be substituted for the dovetails.)
5. Cut the dados in each side to receive the back piece.
6. Cut out the drawer bottom from a piece of plywood.
7. Fit all pieces together before gluing.
8. Glue and clamp the front, sides, and back.
9. Slide the bottom in from the back and nail it to the back piece.

Handle for the drawer

1. Obtain a piece of hardwood, $1\frac{1}{2}'' \times 1\frac{1}{2}'' \times 16''$. This piece is for two handles.
2. Rip this piece to the cross-sectional shape as shown in the drawing. This is done by taking a series of straight and bevel cuts.
3. Cut this section into two 8'' lengths.
4. Sandpaper the drawer pull and fasten it in place on the drawer front with screws from the inside.

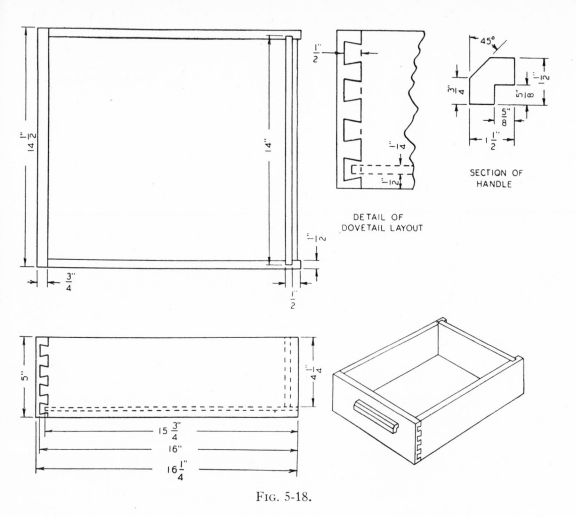

DETAIL OF
DOVETAIL LAYOUT

SECTION OF
HANDLE

Fig. 5-18.

19. COCKTAIL TABLE

This table is of convenient size to use in the living room or in the sun parlor. It can be made almost entirely on the table saw and provides for some interesting operations during its construction. The style of this table suggests that it might be made of a hardwood, such as oak, maple, or birch, and given a blond finish.

Materials Needed:

4 pc., legs:	$1\frac{1}{8}'' \times 2\frac{1}{2}'' \times 18\frac{1}{4}''$	hardwood
2 pc., cross rails:	$1\frac{1}{8}'' \times 2\frac{1}{2}'' \times 25''$	hardwood
1 pc., top:	$1\frac{1}{8}'' \times 18'' \times 35''$	hardwood
8 pc., dowel rod:	$\frac{1}{2}'' \times 2\frac{1}{2}''$	

Procedure (see Fig. 5-19):

1. Square the top to the required dimensions.
2. Square the two cross rails to the required dimensions.
3. Lay out the angles to be cut on each end, as follows:

   a. Measure and mark a distance of $1\frac{1}{4}$ inches in from each end on one edge of each cross rail.

   b. Connect this mark with a straight line to the opposite edge at the corner of the stock.
4. With the aid of the cross-cut guide, cut the angles to the line.
5. On the underside of the top, lay out diagonal lines from corner to corner.
6. Mark a center line on the ends of each cross rail.
7. Place one of the cross rails on its edge directly on one of the diagonal lines and exactly in the center of the cross rail. Make sure that there is an equal distance from each corner of the top.
8. Place the second cross rail on its edge on top of the first cross rail and exactly over the second diagonal line.
9. With a sharp pencil or knife point, mark off the angle at which the pieces cross.
10. Extend the lines across the width of each cross rail.
11. With the aid of the cross-cut guide, cut the half-lap joint.
12. Square the four legs to the required dimensions.
13. Lay out and cut the taper on each leg.
14. Lay the cross rails flat on the work bench and place a leg at each end of the cross rails. Mark off the angle on the top end of the leg to form a straight line with the top edge of the cross rail.
15. Place a straightedge across the bottom of the legs and mark off the bottom angle.
16. Set the cross-cut guide and cut the proper angles on the ends of each leg.
17. Lay out and make the dowel joints. Glue and clamp the legs to the rails.
18. Sand all parts thoroughly.

19. Assemble the cross rails and fasten the rail and leg assembly to the underside of the top with screws. Holes for the screws should be counterbored to one-half the depth of the rail.

20. Sand the entire table and finish as desired.

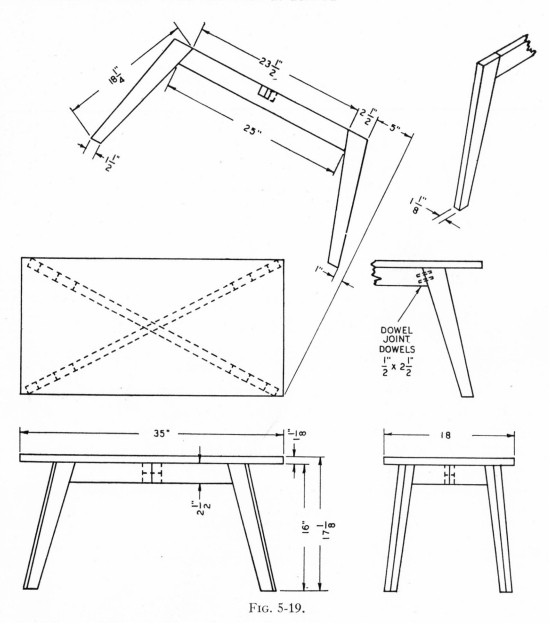

FIG. 5-19.

20. SIDE TABLES

This project is designed to be made in pairs and to be placed at the ends of a couch with a lamp on each table for reading purposes. The tables are especially suited for use at a summer bungalow, and it is suggested that they be made of knotty pine. The construction is quite rugged and will withstand considerable abuse. It is also suggested that a plastic formica top be used to guard against damage by alcohol, cigarettes, etc. The finish can be a coat of shellac and clear lacquer or a varnish.

Materials Needed for Each Table:

4 pc., legs:	$1\frac{1}{4}'' \times 3\frac{1}{2}'' \times 24''$	pine
2 pc., side rails:	$1\frac{1}{4}'' \times 7\frac{1}{2}'' \times 10\frac{1}{2}''$	pine
1 pc., cross rails:	$1\frac{1}{4}'' \times 7\frac{1}{2}'' \times 7\frac{1}{2}''$	pine
2 pcs., frame for top: (sides)	$1\frac{1}{2}'' \times 2'' \times 24''$	pine
2 pcs., frame for top: (ends)	$1\frac{1}{2}'' \times 2'' \times 15''$	pine
1 pc., formica glued on $\frac{3}{4}''$ plywood panel:	$12'' \times 21''$	

Procedure (see Fig. 5-20):

Legs: Get out four pieces as indicated on the drawing for the legs, making the angle cuts by the use of the cross-cut guide and the taper cuts by use of the jig for taper sawing. Round the corners on the shaper, or by hand, as indicated on the drawing. In rounding the corners on the inside of the leg, be sure not to carry the round up beyond the side rails. It should be left slightly below these rails and carried up to them by hand after the legs and side rails have been assembled. Lay out and bore the holes for dowels.

Side rails: Get out two pieces, as indicated on the drawing, for the side rails. Angle cuts may be made with the aid of the cross-cut guide.

Locate the dowel holes by squaring a cross from the previously layed-out holes in the legs. Be sure that the center lines match. Round the bottom corners of the rails on the shaper or by hand.

Cross rails: Get out cross rail as indicated on the drawing.

Top: Get out the band around the formica top, as indicated in the detailed drawing. This will include the rabbeting for the top formica panel, the miter cuts on the ends, and the rounds on the edges. The miter cuts on the ends can be fastened together by clamp nails, spline joints, or dowels. It would be well to screw up through the bottom edge of the rabbeted joint into the top, and assemble the formica top on the decorative frame by using wood screws from the under side of the top.

Assembly: (Smooth and sand all parts.)

1. Saw four dowels to be used between the legs and the top side rail. Push the dowels in place to see that everything is fabricated correctly. While in this as-

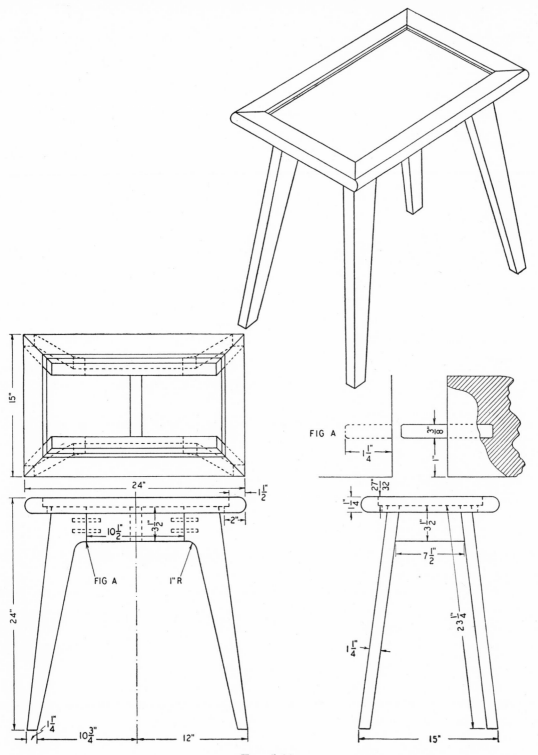

FIG A

FIG A

15"

24"

24"

1½"

2"

10½"

3½"

FIG A   1"R

1¼"

10¾"

12"

1¼"

27/32

3½"

7½"

2¾"

1¼"

15"

3"/8

1"

Fig. 5-20.

93

sembled position, get out two wedges that will be used in clamping the legs to the side rail. The purpose of the wedges is to make a parallel clamping surface so as to prevent the clamps from sliding.

2. After making sure that the fabrication is correct, glue and clamp the assembly together.

3. After the glue has dried, remove the clamps, and excess glue.

4. Clamp the two pairs of assembled legs together with the cross rail between the two side rails. The cross rail can be held in place by using wood screws from the outside rails with the counterbored holes plugged after assembly.

5. Assemble the top with the formica panel in place, and when the glue dries, turn the leg assembly upside down on the top and toe-screw in place.

6. The table should be inspected and sanded over for preparation for finishing. When this is complete, the finishing operation should be performed.

Note: If the four legs do not set steady on a flat surface, this can be fixed by placing the long leg on a piece of coarse sandpaper and scrubbing until all four legs set firmly.

7. Finish as desired.

21. CORNER TABLE

A corner table is practically essential in completing corner balance with sectional davenports. It may also be used as an occasional table between chairs or to "fill out" odd room corners.

Materials Needed:

1 pc., top shelf:	$\frac{7}{8}'' \times 38'' \times 38''$	mahogany
1 pc., bottom:	$\frac{7}{8}'' \times 38'' \times 38''$	mahogany
2 pc., sides:	$\frac{7}{8}'' \times 10\frac{1}{4}'' \times 37\frac{1}{2}''$	mahogany
4 pc., legs:*	$\frac{7}{8}'' \times 3'' \times 16\frac{1}{8}''$	mahogany
4 pc., braces:*	$\frac{7}{8}'' \times 3'' \times 6\frac{1}{2}''$	mahogany
6 pc., edge:	$\frac{1}{4}'' \times \frac{7}{8}'' \times 38''$	mahogany
2 pc., edge:	$\frac{1}{4}'' \times \frac{7}{8}'' \times 4''$	mahogany
1 pc., edge:	$\frac{1}{4}'' \times \frac{7}{8}'' \times 48''$	mahogany

* Made from excess material from top shelf.

Procedure (see Fig. 5-21):

1. Using the cross-cut saw and the cut-off guide, cut a number of pieces of $\frac{7}{8}''$ mahogany to a length of 38''. The number of pieces will depend upon the individual widths of the boards, as they are to form the top and bottom shelves. Veneer-surfaced plywood would be structurally better and easier to fabricate for the shelves.

2. Joint the edges of all boards.

3. Dowel, glue, and clamp the boards edge-to-edge to form the top and bottom shelves. A doweling jig would be a very helpful tool.

4. Square the shelves to 38'' × 38''. They may be trimmed to width, using the rip saw and ripping fence. The ends may be lightly trimmed or smoothed square with a hand plane.

5. The top shelf may be cut at an angle as shown in Fig. A or it may have a serpentine edge. Other edge variations are also possible.

6. Saw the sides to width and length. The length will vary, as the craftsman can use different methods of joining the ends. A butt joint or a spline miter joint is recommended.

The width may also vary. The sides may be fastened to the top and bottom shelves with dowels and glue. A stopped tongue-and-groove joint (see Fig. B) is also a good method of assembly, although somewhat more difficult. The simplest method of assembly would be with wood screws. The screws through the top shelf should be counterbored and the holes plugged with a matching or contrasting wood.

7. Saw out four legs as per dimensions. (See taper cutting in Basic Operations.) Any angle which is pleasing to the craftsman may be established. (See suggested shape, Fig. C.)

8. Cut leg braces and fasten to legs with dowels. The legs and braces may be

doweled or screwed into position on the underside of the lower shelf. If more strength is desired, diagonal cross rails may be used instead of the leg braces.

9. If the craftsman so desires, he can cover the edges of the two shelves with thin mahogany strips. (See list of materials.) This is especially desirable if veneer-surfaced plywood is used.

10. Finish as desired.

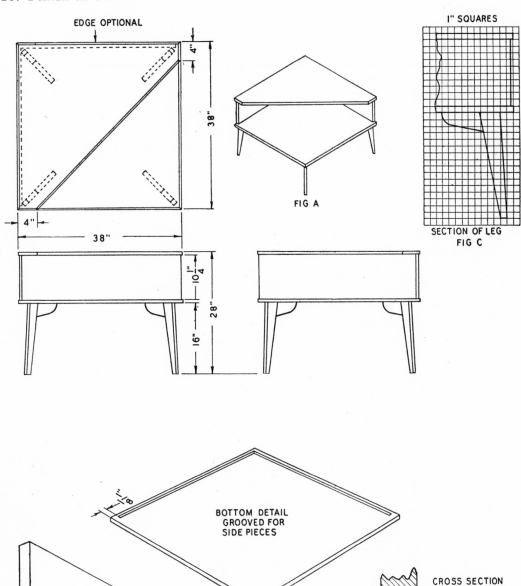

FIG. 5-21.

22. SERVING TABLE

This table makes an ideal coffee table. It may be made from any cabinet wood such as mahogany, walnut, or cherry.

Materials Needed:

4 pc., legs:	$2'' \times 2'' \times 17\frac{1}{8}''$
2 pc., side rails:	$\frac{7}{8}'' \times 2\frac{1}{2}'' \times 24''$ (add extra for tenons)
2 pc., end rails:	$\frac{7}{8}'' \times 2\frac{1}{2}'' \times 14''$ (add extra for tenons)
1 pc., table top:	$\frac{7}{8}'' \times 18'' \times 28''$
2 pc., side leaves:	$\frac{7}{8}'' \times 6'' \times 28''$
2 pc., end leaves:	$\frac{7}{8}'' \times 6'' \times 18''$
8 polished brass hinges:	$\frac{1}{2}'' \times 1\frac{5}{8}''$

Procedure (see Fig. 5-22):

1. Cut legs to size.
2. Lay out and cut all mortises.
3. Saw all rails to dimension. Be sure to allow for tenons.
4. Cut tenons on ends of all rails.
5. Square-up table top. It may be necessary to edge-glue several pieces together to make the top.
6. Sand, assemble, glue and clamp framework together. Fasten top to framework. If wood screws are used the rails must be counterbored.
7. Lay out curved patterns for the leaves.
8. Cut leaves to shape. A band saw may be used or they may be cut by hand. The leaves may also be roughed out on the power saw by freehand sawing on a tangent to the layout line.
9. Sand leaves and fasten to top with hinges.
10. Finish table as desired.

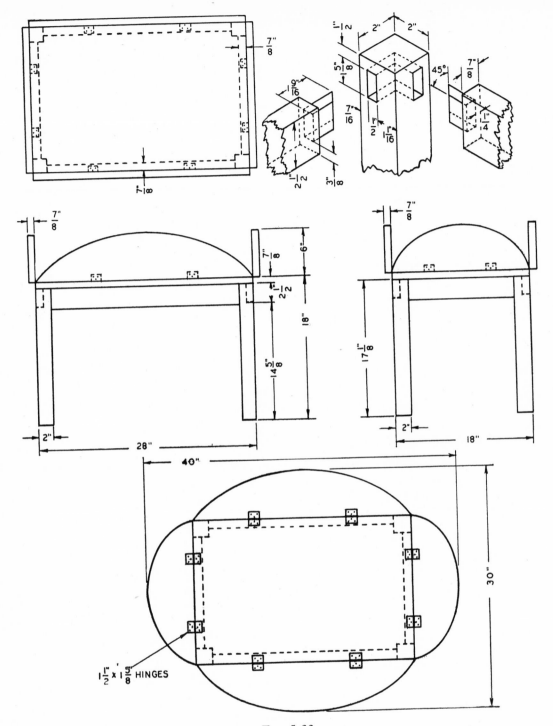

Fig. 5-22.

99

23. STEP TABLE

This table is ideal for an occasional piece to be used at the ends of davenports. It can serve as a coffee table as well. Any cabinetwood can be used.

Materials Needed:

    4 pc., tapered legs (see drawing) cut from 4-2″ × 3½″ × 17″ approximately (a full-size layout pattern should be made of the leg before machining as it may be cut from a smaller piece)

    1 pc., table top: ¾″ × 20″ × 34″

    2 pc., end rails: ¾″ × 2½″ × 14″ (add extra for tenons)

    2 pc., side rails: ¾″ × 2½″ × 29″ (add extra for tenons)

    1 pc., center board: ¾″ × 11¼″ × 13″

    1 pc., back board: ¾″ × 18″ × 11⅝″ (*note:* the grain of this piece should run vertically)

    1 pc., top board: ¾″ × 15″ × 18″

Procedure (see Fig. 5-23):

    1. Get out stock for the four legs. The leg may be cut on a band saw or free-hand saw to layout. (See basic operations.)

    2. Lay out and cut mortises in all four legs.

    3. Rip out and square stock for end and side rails.

    4. Cut tenons on both ends of all rails.

    5. Sand all legs and rails. Assemble, glue and clamp legs and rails.

    6. Square table top to size. It may be necessary to edge-glue several pieces of stock together to make the top.

    7. Sand top.

    8. Square up stock for back board and top board.

    9. Cut center board to size. (See drawing.)

    10. Rabbet top piece.

    11. Sand all pieces.

    12. Fasten center board to top board with dowels and glue.

    13. The back board may be fastened to this assembly with glue and wood screws.

    14. Fasten the whole top assembly to the table top with wood screws driven from the under side of the table top.

    15. The table top may now be fastened to the frame work. If wood screws are used the rails must be counterbored.

    16. Sand and finish as desired.

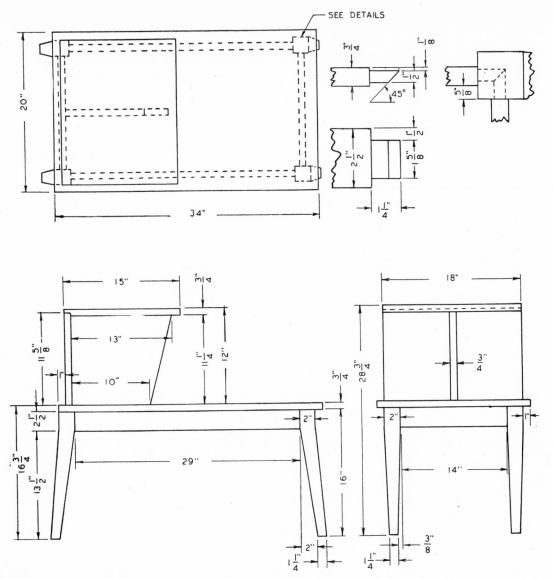

Fig. 5-23.

101

24. GATE-LEG DROP-LEAF TABLE

A gate leg table is a very ornamental and useful piece of furniture. It may be used for a great variety of purposes and is very economical of space because of its folding feature.

Materials Needed:

6 pc., legs:	$2\frac{1}{2}''$	$\times\ 2\frac{1}{2}'' \times 30''$	mahogany
2 pc., end rails:	$\frac{7}{8}''$	$\times\ 6'' \times 9''$	mahogany
2 pc., side rails:	$\frac{7}{8}''$	$\times\ 6'' \times 27\frac{1}{2}''$	mahogany
2 pc., gate rails:	$\frac{7}{8}''$	$\times\ 6'' \times 18''$	mahogany
2 pc., gate stops:	$\frac{5}{8}''$	$\times\ 1'' \times 6''$	mahogany
2 pc., hinge blocks:	$\frac{7}{8}''$	$\times\ 6'' \times 1\frac{11}{16}''$	mahogany
1 pc., table top:	$\frac{7}{8}''$	$\times\ 16\frac{3}{4}'' \times 36''$	mahogany
2 pc., drop leafs:	$\frac{7}{8}''$	$\times\ 22\frac{3}{4}'' \times 36''$	mahogany
6 table top hinges:	$2''$ hinge length $\times 3\frac{13}{16}''$		iron
2 pins:	$\frac{1}{8}''$	$\times\ 6''$	steel
10 table top fasteners.			

Procedure (see Fig. 5-24):

1. Prepare the stock for the six legs and square the legs off to size.
2. Saw the tapers on the legs. Refer to basic operations for instruction for using a tapering jig.
3. Saw out the end, side and gate rails.
4. Lay out and cut the mortises in the legs. Notice that the gate legs have only one mortise apiece.
5. Saw the tenons on the rails. The gate rails have tenons on one end only.
6. If conventional table top fasteners are to be used, a suitable groove should be cut along the inside surface of the table rails about $\frac{1}{2}''$ from the top.
7. Assemble all joints to test for fit.
8. Dissemble the joints and sand all pieces. Then glue and clamp the table frame together.
9. Saw out the gate hinge blocks and make the hinge cuts according to detail "B". Also make the hinge cuts on one end of the gate rails.
10. Round off the ends of the hinge pieces and bore the screw holes in the hinge blocks. Bore the holes for the hinge pins.
11. Glue and clamp the gate legs to the rails.
12. Attach the hinge blocks. These blocks must be positioned so that the gate legs will just swing inside the table legs.
13. Make the gate stop blocks. These blocks will later be attached to the drop leaves so that the gate legs will swing out approximately to the center of the drop leaves to insure maximum support.
14. Saw the table top and drop leaves to size and round off the corners where indicated on the drop leaves.

15. Make the drop leaf rule joints (table leaf joint). The convex portion of this joint which is on the table top can be cut in two steps. First remove a rectangular section (rabbet) on the circular saw and then lay out and plane the curved surface by hand. Finish with sandpaper. The concave surfaces on the drop leaves can be cut by the core box method described in basic operations or they may be done by removing most of the stock with a chamfer cut and then finishing with a hand gouge and sandpaper. This cut may also be made with special cutters for the molding head.

16. Sand all parts thoroughly.

17. Attach drop leaves to table top with table top hinges. See detail A. The position of these hinges can be determined by clamping a hinge to the table top and drop leaf at each end and then moving them a slight amount, until the drop leaf opens and closes correctly. The two end hinges are set in from the edge by about one inch. Mark screw positions and drill pilot holes. Drive screws and test hinge action. The middle hinge is then attached.

18. Fasten the table top to the frame. Insert the fasteners in the rail grooves and mark positions for pilot holes. Use three fasteners in the sides and two in the ends. Drive the screws.

19. Finish as desired.

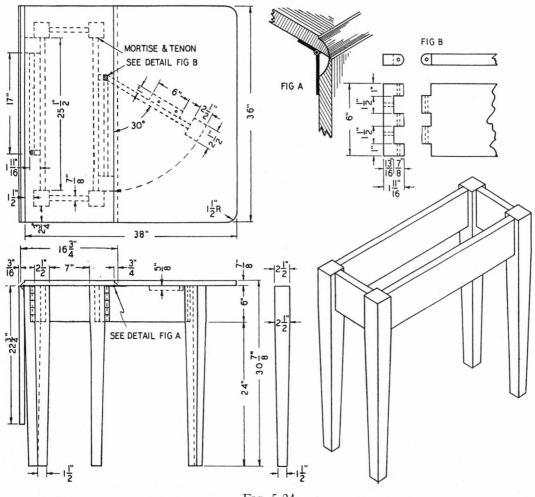

FIG. 5-24.

103

25. CABINET FOR DINETTE

This colonial cabinet may be used either in a dinette or kitchen for storing dishes and silverware. The design may be altered slightly to suit the particular need. If it is to be used for counter space in the kitchen, the top of the base may be surfaced with linoleum or some other plastic surface to match the other cabinets in the room.

Materials Needed:

2 pc., base stand (front & back):	$1\frac{1}{2}'' \times 3\frac{1}{2}'' \times 28''$	pine
2 pc., base stand (sides):	$1\frac{1}{2}'' \times 3\frac{1}{2}'' \times 18''$	pine
2 pc., cabinet base (sides):	$\frac{3}{4}'' \times 19\frac{1}{4}'' \times 34\frac{1}{2}''$	plywood
1 pc., cabinet base (bottom):	$\frac{3}{4}'' \times 19'' \times 30\frac{1}{2}''$	plywood
1 pc., cabinet base (shelf):	$\frac{3}{4}'' \times 17'' \times 30\frac{1}{2}''$	plywood
1 pc., cabinet base (top):	$\frac{3}{4}'' \times 20\frac{1}{2}'' \times 33\frac{1}{2}''$	plywood
2 pc., doors:	$\frac{3}{4}'' \times 14\frac{3}{8}'' \times 23\frac{3}{4}''$	plywood
2 pc., cabinet base front frame (stiles):	$\frac{3}{4}'' \times 2\frac{1}{2}'' \times 34\frac{1}{2}''$	pine
2 pc., cabinet base front frame (rails):	$\frac{3}{4}'' \times 2'' \times 27\frac{1}{2}''$	pine
1 pc., cabinet base front frame (bottom rail):	$\frac{3}{4}'' \times 2\frac{1}{2}'' \times 27\frac{1}{2}''$	pine
1 pc., cabinet base front frame (middle stile):	$\frac{3}{4}'' \times 2\frac{1}{2}'' \times 5''$	pine
2 pc., center guide rail:	$\frac{3}{4}'' \times 2\frac{1}{4}'' \times 19''$	hardwood
2 pc., top drawer guide:	$\frac{3}{4}'' \times 2\frac{1}{4}'' \times 19''$	pine
2 pc., center drawer guide:	$\frac{1}{2}'' \times \frac{3}{4}'' \times 19''$	hardwood
2 pc., drawer fronts:	$\frac{3}{4}'' \times 5\frac{3}{4}'' \times 13\frac{1}{4}''$	pine
4 pc., drawer sides:	$\frac{1}{2}'' \times 4\frac{3}{4}'' \times 19''$	pine
2 pc., drawer backs:	$\frac{1}{2}'' \times 4'' \times 11\frac{1}{2}''$	pine
2 pc., drawer bottoms:	$\frac{1}{4}'' \times 11\frac{1}{2}'' \times 19''$	plywood
2 pc., top assembly (sides):	$\frac{3}{4}'' \times 9\frac{1}{2}'' \times 31\frac{1}{2}''$	pine
2 pc., top assembly (shelf):	$\frac{3}{4}'' \times 9\frac{1}{4}'' \times 31''$	pine
1 pc., top assembly (top):	$\frac{3}{4}'' \times 11'' \times 33\frac{1}{2}''$	pine
2 pc., front assembly pc. (sides):	$\frac{3}{4}'' \times 4'' \times 31\frac{1}{2}''$	pine
1 pc., front assembly pc. (top):	$\frac{3}{4}'' \times 4'' \times 32''$	pine
1 pc., back:	$\frac{1}{4}'' \times 31'' \times 66\frac{3}{4}''$	fir plywood
2 pr., offset cabinet hinges for doors (styles to suit)		
2 door handles (style to suit)		
2 drawer pulls (style to suit)		
1 set friction catch for door (style to suit)		
4 angle brackets:	$\frac{1}{2}'' \times 2'' \times 2''$	steel

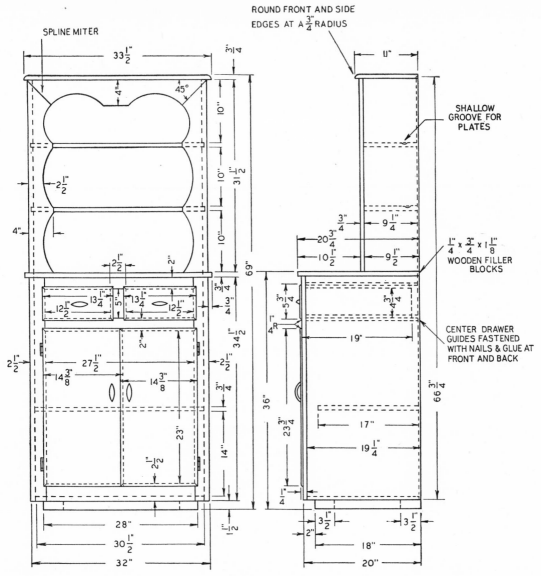

FIG. 5-25(a).

105

Procedure (see Fig. 5-25):

Cabinet Base:

1. Cut the stock for the base stand, miter the ends and assemble it with nails and glue.
2. Get out stock for front frame. Bore for two $\frac{3}{8}''$ × 3'' dowels in each joint. Assemble with glue and clamps. Be sure to test for squareness before glue sets.
3. Cut the stock for the sides, shelf and bottom.
4. Rabbet the side pieces to receive the back.
5. Assemble the front frame, bottom, sides and shelf, using nails and glue.
6. Prepare the stock for the top of cabinet base and fasten it in place, using nails and glue.
7. Make up the two drawers. (See procedure described in project No. 18.)
8. Cut stock for the two doors and rabbet the edges as indicated.
9. Round the corners of the doors as indicated. This might be done with a molding cutter.
10. Hang the doors, following instructions which come with the hardware.
11. Fasten cabinet base to base stand with nails.

Top Assembly:

1. Prepare stock for the front scallop pieces.
2. Cut the miter and spline joint.
3. Lay out and cut the scalloped design on a band or jig saw.
4. Glue the miter spline joints.
5. Prepare the stock for the two shelves.
6. Saw a shallow groove in each shelf for plates.
7. Cut out stock for sides.
8. Rabbet these to receive the back.
9. Make dado cuts to receive the shelves.
10. Cut out piece for the top.
11. Rabbet this piece to receive the back. (Note that this is a stop-rabbet joint.)
12. Round the front and side of the top edges as indicated.
13. Assemble the top shelves with glue and nails.

Assembly:

1. Fasten the top assembly to the cabinet base with angle brackets. (If the cabinet base top is to be surfaced with linoleum or other material, this should be done before the shelves are fastened.)
2. Cut and fit the back piece and fasten it into place with glue and nails.
3. Prepare and fasten wooden filler blocks on cabinet base top. See note on drawing.
4. Prepare the stock for the center-guide rails for the drawers.
5. Cut the required groove in these rails.

6. Fasten these in place with nails and glue.
7. Prepare stock for the center-drawer guide.
8. Fasten this to the drawer bottom with glue and nails.
9. Sandpaper all surfaces.
10. Paint or stain as desired.

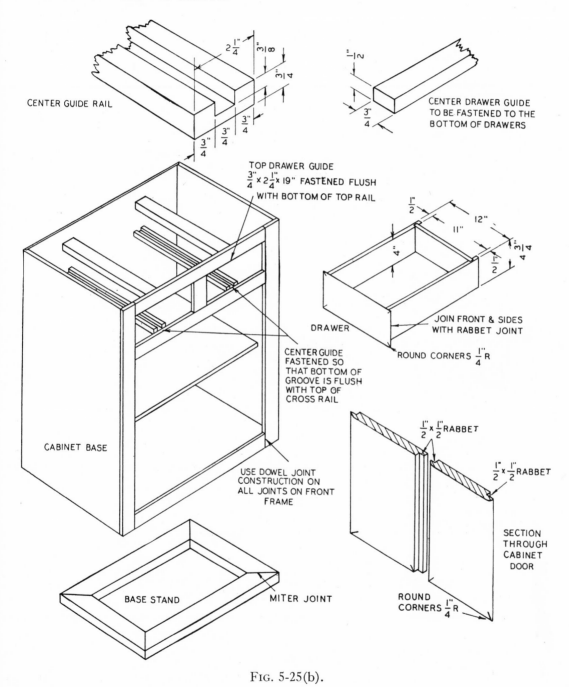

FIG. 5-25(b).

26. RECORD CABINET

A record cabinet is a useful piece of furniture in the home where there is an interest in music. The cabinet outlined is not difficult to make if the following procedure is carried out. It can be made from mahogany, walnut, maple, or any wood that may be appropriate to the room in which it is to be kept.

Materials Needed:

1 pc., top:	$\frac{3}{4}'' \times 16'' \times 34''$	mahogany
1 pc., shelf:	$\frac{3}{4}'' \times 15\frac{3}{4}'' \times 33\frac{1}{4}''$	mahogany
1 pc., bottom:	$\frac{3}{4}'' \times 16'' \times 34''$	mahogany
2 pc., sides:	$\frac{3}{4}'' \times 16'' \times 19\frac{1}{4}''$	mahogany
2 pc., side molding:	$\frac{3}{4}'' \times \frac{5}{8}'' \times 19\frac{1}{4}''$	mahogany
2 pc., top & bottom:	$\frac{3}{4}'' \times \frac{5}{8}'' \times 34''$	mahogany
4 pc., legs:	$1\frac{3}{4}'' \times 1\frac{3}{4}'' \times 2''$	mahogany
1 pc., back:	$\frac{1}{4}'' \times 18\frac{1}{2}'' \times 33\frac{1}{4}''$	plywood

Procedure (see Fig. 5-26):

1. Cut the material to size.
2. Make the dado on the top and bottom pieces of the cabinet and make a rabbet on both ends of the side pieces.
3. Make the dado in the side pieces for the shelf.
4. Rabbet the bottom, top and two ends to receive the plywood back panel.
5. Sand all parts.
6. Glue and clamp the top, bottom, two ends and shelf and wipe off excess glue. While this glue is drying, the rest of the machining can be finished.
7. Miter the molding pieces for the front; cut the taper on the legs.
8. After 24 hours, remove the clamps from the assembled cabinet and scrape off all excess glue.
9. Fasten the mitered molding pieces to the cabinet by use of glue and brads. The brad holes can be filled with stick shellac, or putty mixed to the right color.
10. Glue and screw each of the legs in the position indicated on the drawing.
11. Nail the back in position.
12. Prepare all surfaces for sanding and finish as desired.

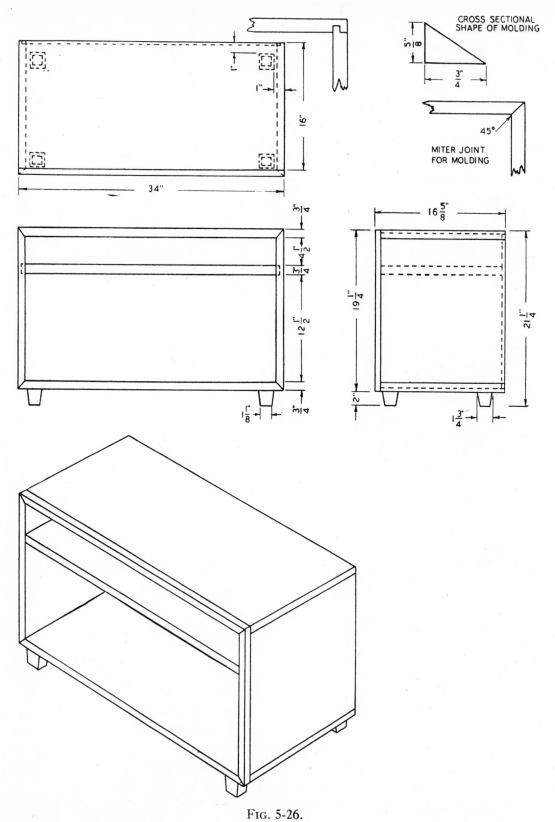

CROSS SECTIONAL
SHAPE OF MOLDING

MITER JOINT
FOR MOLDING

Fig. 5-26.

109

27. TIERED BOOKCASE

This bookcase is one that can be set on the floor against the wall and may be easily moved if one desires to change the position of the furniture in the room. It can be made of mahogany, oak, pine or whatever material will go well with the room in which it is to be used. Pine is used in this project because it is assumed the bookcase will be painted.

Materials Needed:

1 pc., back:	$\frac{3}{8}'' \times 30\frac{5}{8}'' \times 45''$	plywood
3 pc., shelves:	$\frac{3}{4}'' \times 10'' \times 45''$	pine
1 pc., shelf:	$\frac{3}{4}'' \times 10\frac{3}{8}'' \times 45''$	pine
2 pc., base pieces, front and back:	$\frac{3}{4}'' \times 3'' \times 35''$	pine
2 pc., base ends:	$\frac{3}{4}'' \times 3'' \times 8''$	pine
2 pc., center supports:	$\frac{3}{4}'' \times 6'' \times 10''$	pine
1 pc., center support:	$\frac{3}{4}'' \times 6'' \times 8''$	pine
18 center support screws:	$1\frac{1}{2}'' \times 6''$ flathead	iron

Procedure (see Fig. 5-27):

1. Cut all the pieces to size as listed above.
2. Rabbet top shelf.
3. Round the corner of the shelves the radius indicated. This can be done by the use of the handsaw, spoke shave, and file.
4. Miter the base piece.
5. Sand all parts.
6. Assemble the base pieces by use of glue and brads.
7. Fasten the base pieces to the bottom shelf in the correct position as shown on the drawing.
8. Lay out the position of the center support that is to rest on the bottom shelf and locate three screw holes that are to be used for fastening this piece to the shelf.
9. Bore the shank holes for these screws and locate the pilot holes in the center support.
10. Repeat the operation on the other end of the center piece to fasten it to shelf #2. You will note that after shelf #2 is screwed to the center piece, it is impossible to put screws in the second center support straight up through in the same manner in which the screws were put in for the bottom support. Toe screws must be used in this case. When drilling the shank holes for the toe screws, bore the hole at an angle so slight that the hole will not go through the opposite side of the center piece. Pilot holes should be drilled for all screws. This same operation will be needed on the next shelf to hold it to the center piece.
11. After drilling all pilot holes, assemble the shelves with screws and glue.
12. Put on the back piece with brads and glue.
13. After the glue is dry, scrape off all excess, sand for finish, and finish as

desired. Be sure when sanding that the end grain of the shelves and the side grain of the plywood is sanded very smoothly.

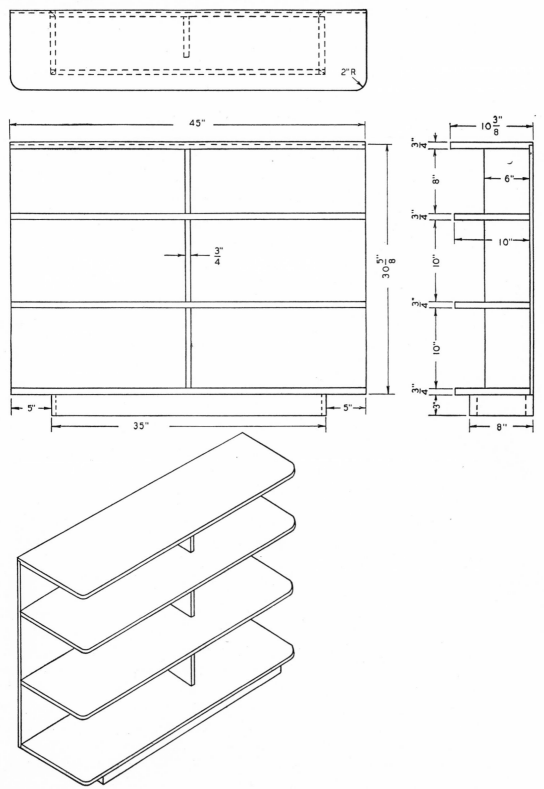

Fig. 5-27.
111

28. MACHINIST'S TOOL CHEST

This tool chest is extremely useful for the home workshop mechanic for storing small tools. It is not difficult to make but requires the accurate machining of many duplicate parts. The design and the dimensions may be modified to satisfy the needs of the individual.

Materials Needed:

2 pc., ends:	$\frac{1}{2}'' \times 11'' \times 13''$	oak
2 pc., top and bottom:	$\frac{1}{2}'' \times 11'' \times 26''$	oak
1 pc., back:	$\frac{1}{2}'' \times 13'' \times 25\frac{1}{2}''$	oak
1 pc., front rail:	$\frac{1}{2}'' \times 3\frac{3}{4}'' \times 26''$	oak
2 pc., sides of front panel:	$\frac{1}{2}'' \times 1\frac{3}{4}'' \times 23\frac{1}{2}''$	oak
2 pc., ends of front panel:	$\frac{1}{2}'' \times 1\frac{1}{2}'' \times 9\frac{1}{4}''$	oak
1 pc., center of front panel:	$\frac{1}{4}'' \times 7\frac{1}{4}'' \times 23''$	oak plywood
1 pc., tray bottom:	$\frac{1}{4}'' \times 10\frac{1}{2}'' \times 25\frac{1}{2}''$	plywood
1 pc., center support:	$\frac{1}{2}'' \times 3\frac{1}{2}'' \times 9''$	oak
4 pc., small drawer front:	$\frac{1}{2}'' \times 1\frac{5}{8}'' \times 12\frac{1}{4}''$	oak
4 pc., small drawer back:	$\frac{1}{2}'' \times 1\frac{5}{8}'' \times 12\frac{1}{4}''$	oak
1 pc., drawer front:	$\frac{1}{2}'' \times 2\frac{1}{4}'' \times 25''$	oak
1 pc., drawer back:	$\frac{1}{2}'' \times 2\frac{1}{4}'' \times 25''$	oak
1 pc., drawer front:	$\frac{1}{2}'' \times 2\frac{7}{8}'' \times 25''$	oak
1 pc., drawer back:	$\frac{1}{2}'' \times 2\frac{7}{8}'' \times 25''$	oak
8 pc., small drawer sides:	$\frac{1}{2}'' \times 1\frac{5}{8}'' \times 8\frac{1}{2}''$	oak
2 pc., drawer sides:	$\frac{1}{2}'' \times 2\frac{1}{4}'' \times 8\frac{1}{2}''$	oak
2 pc., drawer sides:	$\frac{1}{2}'' \times 2\frac{7}{8}'' \times 8\frac{1}{2}''$	oak
12 pc., drawer glides:	$\frac{3}{16}'' \times \frac{1}{2}'' \times 8''$	oak
4 pc., drawer bottoms:	$8\frac{1}{2}'' \times 11\frac{3}{4}''$	18 gage galvanized iron
2 pc., drawer bottoms:	$8\frac{1}{2}'' \times 24\frac{1}{2}''$	18 gage galvanized iron
2 spring pins		
8 knobs (drawer pulls)		
2 carrying handles		
1 piano hinge: $\frac{1}{2}'' \times 26''$		
8 box corners		
1 chest lock.		

Procedure (see Fig. 5-28):

1. Square the two end pieces to the required dimensions.
2. Square the top and bottom pieces to the required dimensions.
3. Square the front rail to the required dimensions.
4. Square the back to the required dimensions.
5. Square the center drawer support to required dimensions.
6. Square the $\frac{1}{4}''$ thick plywood for the tray bottom to required dimensions.
7. Make a $\frac{1}{4}'' \times \frac{1}{2}''$ rabbet on each end and on one edge of the bottom piece to accommodate the back and sides of the chest.

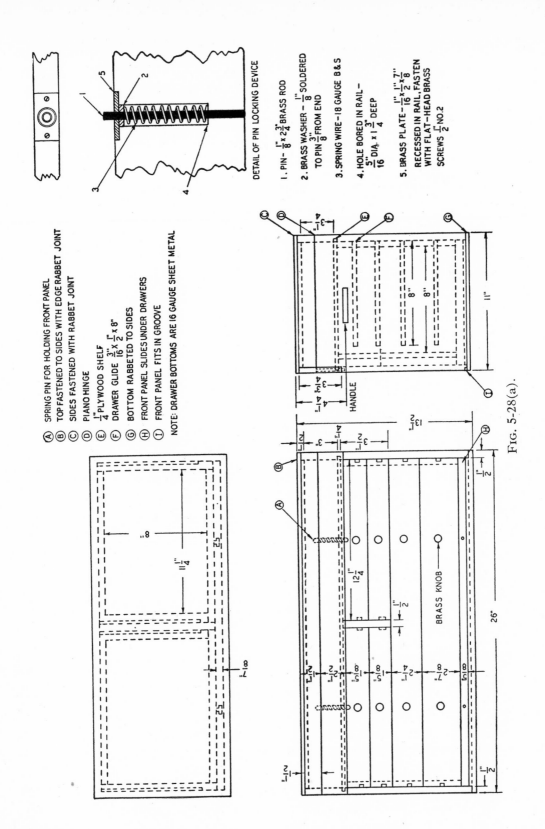

DETAIL OF PIN LOCKING DEVICE

1. PIN — $\frac{1}{8}$" x $2\frac{3}{4}$" BRASS ROD

2. BRASS WASHER — $\frac{1}{8}$" SOLDERED TO PIN $\frac{3}{8}$" FROM END

3. SPRING WIRE — 18 GAUGE B & S

4. HOLE BORED IN RAIL — $\frac{5}{16}$" DIA. x $1\frac{3}{4}$" DEEP

5. BRASS PLATE — $1\frac{1}{16}$" x $\frac{1}{2}$" x $\frac{7}{8}$" RECESSED IN RAIL, FASTEN WITH FLAT—HEAD BRASS SCREWS $\frac{1}{2}$" NO.2

(A) SPRING PIN FOR HOLDING FRONT PANEL

(B) TOP FASTENED TO SIDES WITH EDGE RABBET JOINT

(C) SIDES FASTENED WITH RABBET JOINT

(D) PIANO HINGE

(E) $\frac{1}{4}$" PLYWOOD SHELF

(F) DRAWER GLIDE $\frac{3}{16}$" x $\frac{1}{2}$" x 8"

(G) BOTTOM RABBETED TO SIDES

(H) FRONT PANEL SLIDES UNDER DRAWERS

(I) FRONT PANEL FITS IN GROOVE

NOTE: DRAWER BOTTOMS ARE 16 GAUGE SHEET METAL

FIG. 5-28(a).

HANDLE

BRASS KNOB

8. Make a $\frac{1}{4}'' \times \frac{1}{4}''$ groove the entire length of the remaining edge, $\frac{1}{4}''$ in from the edge of the board. This groove is to hold the front panel.

9. Fasten the two end pieces together by nailing them with several small finishing nails driven near the center of the pieces. This is done so that the rabbets or grooves to be cut on each piece will be adjacent to each other when completed. A cut is made on one side of one piece, then the pieces are turned over and a similar cut is made on the other piece with the same setting.

10. On the front edge of each of the end boards cut a through gain $\frac{1}{2}''$ deep and $3\frac{3}{4}''$ long. This is to accommodate the front rail.

11. On the other edge of each end board, cut a $\frac{1}{4}'' \times \frac{1}{2}''$ rabbet for the chest back.

12. Make a $\frac{1}{4}'' \times \frac{1}{4}''$ groove or stop-dado across the face of each end board $3\frac{1}{4}''$ from the top, stopping $\frac{1}{4}''$ from the back. This groove is to hold the $\frac{1}{4}''$ plywood tray bottom. Remove the nails from the end pieces.

13. Make a $\frac{1}{4}'' \times \frac{1}{4}''$ stop-groove on one face of the front rail $3\frac{1}{4}''$ from the edge to be used as the top of the rail. This groove should start and stop $\frac{1}{4}''$ in from the ends of the piece. This groove is to hold the $\frac{1}{4}''$ plywood tray bottom.

14. Make a $\frac{1}{4}'' \times \frac{1}{2}''$ rabbet on all four edges of the top piece.

15. On the back piece make a similar $\frac{1}{4}''$ groove $3\frac{1}{4}''$ down from the top edge of the piece.

16. Sand all parts.

17. Glue and clamp the ends, top, bottom, front rail, back and plywood tray bottom all at one time as a complete unit. This forms a closed box which will later be sawn apart to form the tray and the lid. Note that the dimensions given on the drawing do not take in consideration the saw kerf. Check for squareness.

18. Using a thin combination saw blade set at approximately $\frac{9}{16}''$ above the table and with the ripping fence set at $1\frac{1}{2}''$, saw completely around the box to remove the lid.

19. Fasten the lid with a length of piano hinge.

20. Fasten the center drawer support with screws applied through the plywood tray bottom and through the back.

21. Square the drawer glides to required dimensions.

22. Square up all parts for the drawers.

23. Cut the rabbets on the ends of all drawer fronts and backs.

24. Cut the grooves for the glides on all drawer sides.

25. Saw a groove $\frac{1}{4}''$ deep, $\frac{1}{8}''$ up from the bottom, of each drawer piece (front, back and sides) to accommodate the sheet metal bottom.

26. Assemble the drawers by gluing and clamping the sides into the front and back rabbets. Be sure to insert the sheet metal bottoms.

27. Sand all drawers.

28. Locate the position of the drawer glides and fasten them to the inside of the tool chest with glue and small finishing nails.

29. Test all drawers for ease of sliding.

30. Square all pieces for the front panel.

31. Make a groove in the side and end pieces to accommodate the center panel.

32. Make haunched mortise and tenon joints for the frame of the panel.

33. Assemble the panel and frame by gluing and clamping.

34. Cut a rabbet on the bottom edge of the panel to fit into the groove in the chest bottom.

35. Fit the panel and locate the holes for the spring pins.

36. Bore the holes for the spring pins in the front rail, and the top edge of the front panel.

37. Insert the spring pins.

38. Sand the entire project and finish as desired.

39. Apply all hardware; handles, drawer knobs and box corners as desired.

40. Line all drawers with thin felt or with flock.

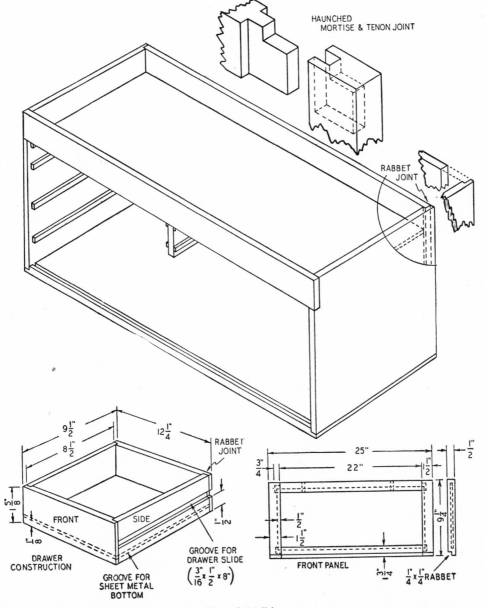

FIG. 5-28(b).

Index